EDITOR: *Charleen Whisnant*

ASSOCIATE EDITOR: *Barbara Campbell*

ART EDITOR: *Joseph Thompson*

EDITORIAL CONSULTANTS: *William Blackburn, John Carr, Fred Chappell, Harriet Doar, Bertha Harris, Amon Liner, Reynolds Price, Ralph Smith, Max Steele*

STAFF: *Bob Beaty, Rebecca Brown, Marion Cannon, Marion Copeland, Harriett Fortenberry, Doris Knauff, Frank McAlister, Marj McDonald, Robert Parati, William Prescott, Joyce Swanzey, Deane Wright*

PRODUCTION: *Homer Baucom, Ellis Edwards, Bruce Funderburk, David Ramsey, Jerry Tadlock*

THE RED CLAY READER 6

RED CLAY READER is published by Southern Review, a non-profit corporation formed to support Southern writing.

Copies of this sixth collection are available at $5.00 each from 6366 Sharon Hills Road, Charlotte, North Carolina 28210

RED CLAY READER welcomes contributions of money (patrons, $10 or more-tax deductible) and manuscripts. Unsolicited material must be accompanied by return postage.

Legal Counsel: Mark Bernstein, Law Building, Charlotte, North Carolina

Manufactured in the United States of America.

Photograph by Phil Morgan

Contents

THE RED CLAY READER 6

"WHEN YOU'VE GONE AS FAR AS PENLAND YOU'VE GONE ABOUT AS FAR AS YOU CAN GO."

By Jonathan Williams

Lord, Lord, O Lord yes!—seems like all the people at Penland got the Green-Apple Quickstep and their hands, they be itchy. The banjos are busy; the salt-kilns are roaring at two o'clock in the morning. It's biscuits and buttermilk, red-eye gravy, people sipping beer and rapping, and finding out what Mr. William Blake meant when he said: "Energy is Eternal Delight." The people—one at a time—make Penland, just as people made Black Mountain. People—*in places of quality.* That's why Blake also affirmed: "Great things are done when Men & Mountains meet; this is not done by Jostling in the Street." It is not noted nearly often enough the part the Blue Ridge Mountains of North Carolina play in all this—whether you are going to see Billy Graham *(oi veh),* Charles Olson *(oi* vague),

or Toshiko Takaezu (soy vase). Mountains give you the coves and knobs where you can "retreat." You have to because nobody in the New Nixon America has any time. Too busy trying to "save" it. My mountain neighbor says: "I don't mean to be a-hesitatin you, but I reckon the feller made time, made plenty of it." Geoffrey Chaucer says: "The lyf so short, the craft so long to lerne." The busiest people are the ones with the most time—there's a wide spot in the road near Penland called Loafers Glory. So, you loaf in the hills, invite the soul, perfect your attentions, get crafty. You get your head clear in Buncombe County or Mitchell County. You see better from the sides of mountains, as Chinese poets and painters have been telling us for some thousands of years.

What I want to give you is Penland, *right now.* Penland *then,* you get that from reading *Gift From the Hills* (Miss Lucy Morgan's Story), by LeGette Blythe (The Bobbs-Merrill Company: $5.00). A quick sense of it you might get from some of my pieces in *Craft Horizons* (16 East 52 Street, NYC 10022), particularly the special insert section on the Southern Appalachians in the twenty-fifth anniversary issue, summer 1966 . . . So I took my ears over to Penland this June and used them as sponge-cameras.

First of all, Bill Brown, the zany enthusiast and fearless factotum, who has been director of Penland for the last five or six years: "Except for the ice-machine blowing its top and the damp pump going sour on us, we got off the ground in great style this summer. We've had more people here for the first session than ever before, and we're already ninety per cent full for the whole summer. When we hit 130 for each session, then that's it—otherwise they're coming out the walls and start clawing for each other's food . . . This session went amazingly well. Lots and lots of work done, lots of good feeling. We have that Show & Tell on the last day. Everybody takes everything outdoors, they put the stuff on the lawn and hang it up everywhere. It gives them a chance to see what the other people have been doing, gathering in one place. So they use up a thousand rolls of film taking pictures, and taking pictures of each other—just like Show & Tell for the little kids. We got the good horses here, baby, if you want to run with them. Come on, let's see you try."

Ted Hallman is a nationally recognized weaver. He teaches at the Moore College of Art in Philadelphia. This is his sixth summer at Penland: "Penland is in the tradition of Cranbrook and Haystack, but I think that as of this summer it has surpassed either. It's because of the possibility here of feeling very relaxed and unsophisticated, of not having to perform in a certain fixed way. And people now suddenly know about Penland—it's well established and is running at top capacity. They want to participate . . . This year Barbara Ferguson and I have taught together, very intensively. One of the areas we explored was an environmental thing in which five persons became interested. We got together, each person did a sketch and a model—some kind of weaving and interlacing, a structure you possibly could get into or get encompassed by. The group decided on one person's idea and everybody worked on it. It turned out to be an out-of-doors thing, using trees and sticks and yarns. The plan was a small enclosure in which you could rest or recline, meditate, with an opening at the top for looking at the sky. Plus some sound—wind bells or chimes. That's how it started. We got into it and it grew. There were spaces you got into before you arrived at the small, central retreat-area. And we had a sort of happening in these spaces. We went to a local mill and got 50 pounds of some mill-end material— kind of nylon—and some warp about a yard long. The stuff looked sort of like hair: very, very white. We

suggested that people who wanted to should come that evening at 7:30 and participate in this Nest-In. So they took these fibers and tied them onto the structure, these strings and stuff, and it was really wild. People got very turned on. Some, of course, only stood on the side and gaped. It all happened so quickly. The basic structure was in green yarns and browns and looked like the trees and woods. But this white material was synthetic, so foreign to all that look, the scene became totally unreal. Within twenty minutes people were getting this whiteness all over—you could literally see it growing. Inside, people were sliding around on it. There were billows of it and kids were using it like sliding boards. Some people were throwing it up in the trees; others were climbing the trees and dropping it. Kind of got out of hand. Barbara and I were pretty worried for awhile. . .

"You know, I occasionally ask myself why I keep coming down here year after year. I think the answer is the spirit of the place. It's certainly not for pay. You really work very hard, the students are very demanding, you feel very used. I work much harder here than at Moore, but I couldn't keep up this intensity for more than a few weeks. The last three nights I've been in the studio past two o'clock with people asking questions and still working. I'd say that's incredible."

Toshiko Takaezu is one of our very distinguished craftsmen—a potter/weaver from Clinton, New Jersey, where she lives in a music-hall building. Her studio is below the stage of the theater. It even goes up and down if she wants it to. Might be a happy thought to have her rise out of the depths at the beginning of Beckett's *Play* and throw pots around the three characters who then sit in them and do their monologues. Tosh and I got to joking: "This is my fifth year at Penland and this time Bill Brown decided I could come as 'visiting scholar' and be around with no specific thing to do—except to do my own work. I am hoping to become Miss Mitchell County Local Aesthetic Treasure and wear a special ceramic badge. . . This session has been a great mixture—many husbands and wives, many kids. I've been doing sculpture and bothering them in the woodshop. One thing I did was follow Bill Brown around for two days. I didn't get anywhere."

Bill Brown

Paulus Berensohn

Paulus Berensohn is also a potter. He lives on a farm above Scranton, Pennsylvania, and below Binghamton: "I moved there two years ago on sabbatical from Swarthmore College to stay six months. It looks like it's going to be my permanent home. This is my first experience at Penland. I started out as a dancer—modern, ballet, Broadway shows, Merce Cunningham... When I was thirty I decided I wanted to do something with my hands and not to live in a city. I went for a short visit to Pendell Hill, the adult Quaker community. They had a craft shop but no teacher. One night I went into the shop and threw a pot. The next morning someone asked me how I did it. By that afternoon I had a class. Then for three weeks I taught weaving, potting, and graphics—none of which I had ever done, *really*. Then I went to Haystack Mountain School and studied with M. C. Richards. My teaching is very much influenced by her approach.

"I would describe Penland as a 'Beloved Community.' I've rarely been to a place where there is so much warmth and where there is so little division between age. I think the presence of the children is very important. One little boy started coming to class and he did brilliantly. I actually had him demonstrate the last day. I had been preparing the demonstration. He watched me and imitated me and by the time for the demonstration he was doing it with more skill than I...

"My approach to working is almost diametrically opposed to most of the attitudes here. I am disinterested in the pot after it is made. Clay, for me, is a healing material. I need it in my life. I use it meditatively and therapeutically. That's hard to speak about without sounding 'medical,' which is not where it's at. I can't answer a student in class: is this a good pot or a bad pot?—because for me the aesthetic is the *person* and the person who breathes life into clay. So that a pot that perhaps has a bad rim and a heavy foot can be just breathtaking—if the spirit is in there. Failing can be as exciting, as moving, and as telling as the pot's making it. That's what I am trying very hard to learn how to tell people.

"Let's talk for a minute about Black Mountain and Penland. There is a big difference. This place sows seeds and Black Mountain was a soil in which such seeds could grow. It's, after all, two weeks versus a year or two or three or four. Ideally, Penland would be an open community into which one would come for as long as one needed to stay... When I say that Penland is the 'Beloved Community,' I'm not sure I want to live in a small place forever where we all share food, etc. I think what I really mean is that the atmosphere of support and honesty between people is very special here—of people responding to the gifts of others. I've made friends and fallen in love in this session. *Two* weeks was *all* beautiful. Now if it had been four weeks or eight weeks or a year, the hard side of it would have come in, which is really where all the pith is. And a lot of us with great talents shrink from that. We're talking about an atmosphere of mutual support—that's the Esalen spirit as well—and I am amazed at what eighteen- and twenty-year-olds know about themselves. It seems a number of my contemporaries and I have had to go into our thirties before we are able to stop and look. It has been almost 'too rich' an experience. I mean, I ought to leave now but I can't. I see that little house and the vegetable dyeing and I can't go without learning something from Catherine.

"I would love to find a way to keep the depth of relationship with clay we have begun *alive*, rather than simply starting some eager-beaver syndrome of banging out pots. I would like to have suggested that the last day we put all the pots in a circle and then hold hands and look at the pots for several hours and then break them and not have to fire them. It wouldn't be throwing pots away—*it would be throwing them into a common bond*. But, glazing and firing are part of the story, so I did not suggest this. We ought to get beyond taking home trophies from summer camp, etc.

"I would love to see certain elements that have been learned in places like Esalen brought into Penland, like very simple breathing exercises for the whole community. I know Jane Brown is interested, so probably this will happen. I'd like to see more interdisciplinary things here, like poets and college people and weavers making their own papers... It is obvious that a trained ecologist should be in residence to point out the more elusive connections between things... I don't know whether you read an article by John Leonard in the *New York Times Magazine* a few months ago. It was about Warhol, ostensibly, but spoke about what Leonard thinks is the great message of a man like Warhol—that we all can make our own tapestries, make our own symphonies with tape-recorders and synthesizers, blow our own glass, make our own pots, make our own movies, all to save man from the weight of an automatic response before the new machinery. He defined *craftsmanship* in a lovely way: the self-shaping of privacy. A very intuitive definition, is it not, for surely *facility* is only *one* thing to gain by studying. More importantly, clay and yarn are materials and possible ways of liberation."

Catherine Morony comes from Alamo, in the Rio Grande Valley of Texas. She offers a unique course in vegetable dyeing at Penland. Her cauldrons and cabin are the center of the Ancient Wisdom at the school.

Dogs, children, familiars, and initiates seek out her cheery countenance there. When I talked to Catherine she was busy stirring a pot full of dog-hobble, leaves, stems, twigs, etc. Dog-hobble is what the mountain people call *Leucothoe*, the White Goddess, sacred to Moon Lady, according to Mr. Graves. Oddly, the dye from this plant comes out with a black scum on it and is a darkish green. It can be lighter depending on the various pots—copper, brass, iron—and the chemical reactions therein. If you put in a mordant, or fixative, that again will produce more variations. Alum is the best mordant because it doesn't change the plant's natural color.

"We are finding out some very fascinating things about the rhododendron. We have up to now six colors, of which you can get various shades, using iron sulphate in the iron pot (gray), nickel sulphate in brass pot (tan), alum in the copper pot (yellow). In the fall or winter, if you would fill up the iron pot with rhododendron leaves, and you put in, say, four ounces of wool, you'd come out silver-gray; in the springtime you'd get a greenish gray. In July, which is the greatest month for it, you'd get almost black. Since we dye the whole year round we're more sensitive to these variations than people used to be. They'd maybe do hulls in the winter, barks in the spring, roots in the fall.

"We're about to use the wild coreopsis, broom-sage (a really nice rich yellow), madder root, black-oak bark, fustic (in the mulberry family), and wood chips—that's all that's ready now. Other times, let's see: tulip poplar, apple, cherry, sassafras (roots or bark—a distinctive pinkish tan), bloodroot, marigold blossoms, dahlias. Actually, about the only thing I've tried that wasn't exciting at first was morning-glory—a very light gray-yellow. But I got to like it using it in a tapestry background...You take those roses out there in front of the cabin. Just cut the leaves off and boil them up, they give you a yellow. With the wild coreopsis you use the flower itself. Half a pound of blossoms will do a pound of wool a rust red; more

wool, a lighter one. Oddly, only the first picking will give you a red. Later it's yellow. Dyeing remains very mysterious and the lore has always tended to remain unwritten. For instance, for two years the walnut-hull crop gave me only a tan color, not the familiar rich red-brown. Now it's back to 'normal.' I have no idea what possessed the trees to change their tune. I mean, *tone*...I came here in 1961 and learned from Katie Lewis who learned from Mrs. Conley, a local lady. There are still a few ladies around, but not many. Just as there are almost no yarb-doctors who practice healing by plants."

Adela Akers, weaver, was born in Spain and operated a shop in Chicago before coming to Penland as a resident-craftsman under a program funded by the National Endowment for the Arts: "I've found a year here a marvelous experience. There is so much serenity and so little conflict here, so little distraction, that one produces extraordinary amounts of work. I've found the mountain people very beautiful to be around—much more so than town people or people in the flat country. They are much closer to artists than any other people. Long hair or beards don't mean that much to them, it's just one human characteristic. They are shy but finally very open with me, rather like the Indians I lived among in South America. I like people who can open their doors and talk. They have things to say—restful things to say. About their houses, their animals, their fields. They don't lay 'personal' problems on you, and this is the kind of neighbor I want."

So, take these persons at their word and let's leave Penland at that. On the map you may be able to spot it along the Toe River, about four miles from Spruce Pine, North Carolina. For precise information, write to the Registrar, Penland School, Penland, N. C. 28765. The phone is 704/765-2359. You'll probably get a direct line to Bill Brown, at the bottom of some hole, trying to fathom the latest crisis in the plumbing. Students with plumbing experience get a special discount.

Photographs by Stephen Rose

Photographs by Phil Morgan

BLACK MOUNTAIN COLLEGE

By Roger Wicker

Mark Hopkins' hoary chestnut about a teacher and a student on a log constituting the ideal college has never gained much academic ground in American higher education. And while his idea has been alternately embraced and discredited through the years, it has a lasting value, as shown by the number of small, experimental colleges that have tried his approach, including Mark Hopkins College in Brattleboro, Vt., and the defunct Black Mountain College at Black Mountain, N. C.

In the instance of Black Mountain College, the chestnut sprouted, flourished and fell victim to its own peculiar blight. It pointed out new directions for U.S. higher education in a way that is perhaps best illustrated by contrasting it with the "retrogression" of the Vanderbilt University Agrarian movement. Black Mountain College took its stand for non-political radicalism in higher education; its goal was the development of the individual as a total person of intellect and emotion.

BMC, just outside the present-day town of Black Mountain, approximately eighteen miles from Asheville, was an attempt, from 1933 to 1956, to put into living terms the philosophies of Mark Hopkins and BMC's principal founder, John Andrew Rice. A Southerner and a Rhodes Scholar, Rice was a genuine American educational rebel. His outspoken ideas of education and outrageous manner of agitating for them amounted to a rebellion against the raccoon coat American colleges of the Coca-Cola era of the Twenties and Thirties. Gatsby and F. Scott Fitzgerald would have been most uncomfortable at Black Mountain.

Alden Whitman of the *New York Times,* in Rice's 1968 obituary, declared him a witty, opinionated and thoroughly self-assured intellectual who was convinced that most of his fellow educators were "half-baked thinkers," or worse, "no thinkers at all." In a 1936 statement that came years ahead of the same realization by today's student activists, Rice said, "The center of control in American education has shifted from those who really know something about education, the teachers, to those who in most cases really know nothing about it, the trustees." Generally speaking, American higher education at the time of BMC's founding was centered around the German university ideal—that is, in Rice's words, "stuffing the head full of facts," but not possessing self-knowledge. The European tradition stressed the intellect, and emotional development was largely neglected. The business of helping students develop insight into how to live in and cope with their world and to make their education relevant to the conditions of existence was not then thought worthy of the attention of universities.

"The dividing line," in American higher education, Rice said, was "always the neck. American colleges can be divided into those that are interested in what happens above the neck and those that are concerned with what happens below the neck. At Black Mountain we are concerned for the whole human being." Rice and the founders of Black Mountain were seeking a balance by which Rice meant intelligence— "a subtle balance between the intellect and the emotions." In BMC, Rice was seeking to counterpoise this subtle balance with the Mark Hopkins notion of direct teacher-student interaction.

A close friend of John Dewey, who was a visitor at BMC on several occasions through the years, Rice had taught at several colleges before the Black Mountain experience, honing his insight and refining his educational philosophy. At each of these previous colleges Rice had constantly sniped at sacred academic cows grazing on the campuses. He noted in his autobiography, *I Came Out of the Eighteenth Century,* that most of the colleges where he had taught classics and English literature were glad to see him leave; he was dismissed from Rollins College for "agnostic beliefs, his frank manner of expression, and his occasionally immodest dress" and he described that place as "a liberal college in an illiberal town, with the inevitable conflict when the college has to decide not to be liberal," to avoid offense to its donors.

This was the third college Rice had left under circumstances that did little to further his reputation as the outstanding Socratic teacher he was. One former faculty member at Black Mountain, recalling in recent years Rice and his opinionated ways, commented, "If I'd been Hamilton Holt, I'd have fired him too. He was always meddling, tinkering. He was a troublemaker." Rice's biggest fault was that he could not keep silent on matters of "compulsory mis-education." John Evarts, one of the original faculty members at BMC, described Rice as "alternately an amiable, provocative Socrates and a diabolical rebel and critic . . . . His constant companion was his pipe—which was as stocky as himself. He would often shock people by emptying the burnt tobacco inadvertently on the floor. But he loved to shock people in all ways —to provoke them to think. He would make sweeping statements—usually condemnations—to watch people blink and see how they would defend themselves or their ideas. Like some psychoanalysts he would "break people down"—and not always build them up again. This applied to both students and faculty members. But he was always brilliant and could have the tongue of angels. He was loved, feared, and sometimes hated. A real father figure."

During May and June of 1933, Rice and several faculty members who followed him from Rollins began to develop the idea of forming their own college. Throughout the summer, they formulated the basis for the new experimental college. When it finally opened in September with 10 faculty members and nineteen students, they all breathed deeply for the first time since they had begun to recruit students for a college whose opening date was not even a certainty to its founders. The new college took its name from the Black Mountain Range near Asheville, the site having been suggested at first by Robert Wunsch, former drama instructor in the Asheville City Schools and later a faculty member at Rollins and BMC.

Explaining to a friend in 1933 what he was seeking by the founding of a college on an untried concept, Rice said, "Now look at Mark Hopkins' log. Between the teacher and the student sit as a minimum requirement of all academic logs, a president, a dean of the college, a dean of men and women, and a registrar, all of whom are more or less subject to a board of trustees or regents." Furthermore, the trustees tended to be conservative business men who knew next to nothing about education. Rice and his associates sought to eliminate as many of those "impediments that ordinarily stand between the teacher and the student" as possible. And to that end Black Mountain was owned by its faculty, had no non-teaching presidents, no trustees, no deans, no fraternities or sororities, no arbitrarily imposed rules, no required curriculum and no intercollegiate sports. A professor and his students would decide which courses would be offered each term; if no one was interested in a mathematics course in a given term, none was offered, and no one was required to attend classes, the English university tutorial system being BMC's modified method of class sessions. Class sessions were informal, tending to the seminar approach, often meeting outdoors or in faculty offices. Biology courses wandered down to the college farm to watch the pigs give birth; political science classes journeyed to Washington to confront senators and congressmen with frank questions.

Charles Bell, a Princeton instructor at Black Mountain in the summer of 1947, contrasted Black Mountain's approach with that of St. John's, saying, "Having taught at Black Mountain is an experience worth paying for. One pays in spiritual tension. The sheer fever of living there, of encountering these strange students, of being battered by the communal waves, of living the storm and stress of a consciously progressive anarchy—this cannot be sensibly described. Black Mountain . . . builds in a way the counter-pole to St. John's College. Where St. John's revolution is itself a return to tradition and the past, a planned surrender to the discipline of the great books, that is, an imposed unitary regimen of the mind, Black Mountain's very rupture with tradition is in a sense traditional, a last continuance of the splurge of progressive education. In this it pretends to have no method, no system, but this very attitude implies both method and system, namely of a licentious pluralism, and with a hatred of the St. John's pure and abstract authority. And for the binding regimen of the mind, we have here an orgy of feeling activity. If St. John's has been called impractical and anti-modern, this may be termed hectically practical, wedded to the loosest phases of modernism."

He further noted that at St. John's he was disturbed by a lack of artistic and literary creation, whereas at Black Mountain the only courses that seemed to succeed were those which encouraged the student directly to express himself. This isn't considered especially innovative now, but this was in 1933, three decades before the free university ideal evolved from the Berkeley Free Speech Movement, three decades before students began to demand wide-ranging university reform to make their education relevant and less rigidly structured, and before seminar classes, individualized education, and independent study became the norm rather than the exception in American colleges and universities.

At Black Mountain, dialogue had reached a high level of operation before such faculty-student exchanges had attained the now imperative position in some American colleges and universities and whose absence in others sparks paralyzing student rebellion. In the absence of outside controlling influences, such as trustees, Rice and BMC's founders turned to the idea recently revived by the New Left student activists, that of participatory democracy—where each member of the community, and Black Mountain was a community in most senses of the word, has a voice in making the decisions that govern and determine the scope of his life. Black Mountain's participatory democracy was refined to a board of fellows composed of six faculty members and the chief student officer who was elected by the students as their policy-making voice in the college's affairs. Each year the board of fellows would elect a Rector, an administrative post not unlike that of the ordinary academic dean. Other student officers included four representatives who met once a month with the board of fellows, and oftener if necessary.

Not so long ago, Fred Hechinger of the *New York Times* boldly asserted that "student power" as a viable demand upon the faculty and administration of a college was questionable, because, among other reasons that Black Mountaineers would have immediately rejected, a college population is transient with four-year turnovers in the student body. Yet Black Mountain anticipated the student power demand, and, in fact, thrust it upon its own students unasked for because it was recognized as a necessary part of an organic community of scholars. BMC had a plan for coping with the transient nature of the student body: it was simply that at least half of each year's student body consist of students from the previous year to act as a control group and to initiate the newcomers into the college's sense and fact of community. The same rule of thumb applied to faculty selection.

In the college's application of democracy, there were at first and for many years afterwards no votes taken on matters concerning the entire college. The board of fellows and the student representatives met and discussed the problems facing the college, maintaining all the time close contact with their individual constituencies, which were not always distinct from each other, and in cases of great importance the entire

college community would examine and discuss the matter at hand—often for hours on end, and occasionally informally for days—until a consensus was reached, the theory being that a vote would divide the community into arrogant majorities and disgruntled minorities. Necessarily, group functions of this nature precluded a large student body. The college was kept small (never more than 100 students and often less) to avoid the facelessness and unwieldiness of larger student bodies and to make for a more cohesive community life. Paul Goodman has commented, in *Community of Scholars*, that the Black Mountain "communitias" made it often impossible to distinguish between students and faculty, between married and unmarried members. Years ahead of student protests against the dehumanizing effects of the multiversity and then the megaversity, Black Mountain was seeking to avoid and overcome the myopics of mass education, stressing the importance of the individual's development.

There were no formal graduation requirements, and indeed the college did not confer degrees or diplomas, and for several years purposely did not seek accreditation. The curriculum was divided into the junior and senior divisions. When, after approximately two years of general studies in the junior division, a student felt ready to concentrate on a major field of study, he requested an oral and written examination designed by the entire faculty. For graduation, a student notified the Rector when he felt ready to leave the community. Outside examiners were called in for intensive examinations, often lasting a week. Such men as Jacques Barzun of Columbia, Stringfellow Barr of St. John's, and Edward Steichen the photographer were among the visitors as examiners at Black Mountain. And they all expressed surprise at the breadth and scope of the knowledge of the Black Mountain students they examined. Not being an accredited school, Black Mountain made arrangements with Columbia, UNC, the University of Chicago and others, for its "graduates" to enter their graduate schools, despite their lack of formal credentials.

Finances at Black Mountain were always uncertain, to say the least, and the work program was the force that held it together, whereas Bell said the Thomistic scheme was what held St. John's intact. Aside from a janitor (who often found professional reasons for looking in on the life studies class), an office worker, and two cooks, Black Mountain was run by the students and faculty. At the evening meals, the main course might be served by a faculty member, students would clear away the dishes and bring the coffee, while another faculty member might fetch the dessert from the kitchen. Students and faculty shared virtually every work-task connected with the college, some assuming for the time they were there a particular chore, such Josef Albers' maintenance of the lawns.

From the beginning, Rice and his associates decided that art would be the center of the college's attention

and curriculum, partially because art was felt by them to be a reflective process. The student must think about what he is going to do, do it, and then reflect upon what he has done. The democratic man, they said, must be an artist. They felt the artist was not a competitor, since his more important struggle was competing with himself. His struggle was inside, not against his fellows, but against his own ignorance and clumsiness, said Rice. At the time of the college's founding in the rented Lee Hall of Blue Ridge Assembly, owned by the Southern YMCA, a uniquely creative teacher was growing uneasy over the growth of Nazism in his native Germany.

Josef Albers began as a student at the Bauhaus in Dessau and later became a master of the school. His dynamic personality and his studies of perception (how forms and colors are perceived and the illusions and distortions thereby involved) were known throughout Europe and attracted students from throughout the Continent. These studies were continued at Black Mountain and later at Yale University where he was head of the design department.

Chafing under Hitler's regime, especially when the Bauhaus was attacked as "degenerate" and "Communist," Albers was seeking a way out of Germany. Through the Metropolitan Museum of Art, he was persuaded to come to Black Mountain after Rice had heard of him quite by chance. Rice acted on the hunch that Albers was the man the college needed to put into effect his ideas on the importance of art in general education. Albers came to Black Mountain, speaking little English, with his wife, Anni, a noted textile designer and weaver, both of them genuine rebels and pathfinders. They fitted in so well with the Black Mountain scheme that they stayed and taught from 1933 to 1949, turning down offers from several more affluent schools that were able to pay whatever salary they might have wished. But they were primarily teachers and the Black Mountain setup was ideal for both. For him, it was ideal for his ideas of teaching art, color and Werklehre (work with materials and forms). During the second World War, anti-German feeling was responsible for the renaming of the materials and form class in English.

A visit to an Albers Werklehre class was described in 1938 by journalist Louis Adamic in *My America*, who said, at first "the work that he and his students do there looks ridiculous . . . they take, let us say, three green bottles, four red apples, a piece of yellow cloth and a lady's slipper, or some such seemingly irrelevant or incongruous group of articles; then work with them, together and individually, trying to arrange them so that each thing enhances the form, line, texture and color values of each of the others, and helps to tie them all together into a well-proportioned, harmonious, effective picture.

"It is, in fact, important training in seeing things, in discrimination, in taste, in acquiring a sense of form, line, color proportion and in handling materials.

"It is also an indirect aid to the students in getting to know themselves and one another, for there are inner reasons why I want to place this bottle here and you there. It is action. Things happen in that class, things that can be seen, touched, changed, analyzed and reflected upon."

Adamic commented that after several months of this sort of art work, the student, when home from college in the summer or on vacation, is able to see in his hometown the same incongruities, not only its architectural, but—if he is a successful Black Mountain student—also its social and spiritual incongruities and disharmonies. "Thus, art instruction at Black Mountain, working jointly with the other elements of the college setup and processes is, in actuality, indirect sociology—sociology grounded in artistic values, which are positive and eternally active in their objection to incongruity."

Drawing classes under Albers were not just drawing classes. Albers realized, for example, that student So-and-So was a timid young person, a victim of all sorts of fears, a product of contemporary family and social conditions and trends. Albers helped the student in subtle ways, part of his teaching technique. He helped him overcome the feeling of fear and uncertainty when faced by a huge sheet of blank drawing paper—the student drew a line, Albers was there, watching, helping, encouraging and joking with him. A few months of Albers' attention and the student begins to draw fairly well, the timidity is gone and he gradually becomes a new person.

By 1936, the college had established a solid reputation in academic and scholarly circles. But in spite of this it remained obscure to the general public. And nowhere, despite an article by Adamic in *Harper's* and later in *Reader's Digest,* was it more obscure than in the Swannanoa Valley where it was located and in nearby Asheville. To those that bothered, it was either a refreshing place, or a hotbed of "communism and free love." It was known as "that place," where people different from the mountain folk were doing things they didn't understand. Though it is defunct and its impact now enormous, most area people are still basically unaware of its importance, much as they were when Thomas Wolfe published *Look Homeward, Angel,* instead dwelling on the "scandalous" aspects of both Wolfe's book and BMC.

In 1937, with the help of financial backers, the college purchased a tract of land across the valley, a summer resort on Lake Eden—now Camp Rockmont for Boys. Walter Gropius and Marcel Breuer were commissioned to design a complex for the Black Mountain lakeside campus, but financial difficulties caused these plans never to be carried out. Architectural models and photographs of the models were as far as the Gropius-Breuer design could go. An alternate plan, utilizing student and faculty labor, was decided upon. Architect A. Lawrence Kocher, a former editor of *Architectural Record,* designed a complex of Inter-

national style buildings for a self-contained college plant. And in 1941, the first of three proposed buildings was completed. Students and faculty had dug the foundation, mixed the concrete and hauled rock for the foundation walls. Under the supervision of Richard Gothe, a German refugee with European work camp experience, the entire college community raised the walls of their sleek new Studies Building. It had approximately 60 individual study rooms for students and faculty on three levels, and a large faculty meeting room was called the Kocher Room in honor of the building's designer. The Studies Building, still in use but in disrepair at Camp Rockmont, was the only one of the Kocher-designed group that was completed. Actually, it was occupied before it was completely finished, and it was never really finished according to the plans.

Robert S. Moore Jr., writing a catalogue foreword for an exhibit of Black Mountain artists at East Tennessee State University in 1966, said the "move [across the valley], which was the college's immediate salvation, brought with it new problems, and was ultimately another factor in the college's decline." For the 700-acre tract destroyed the closeness of the community. The former unity of one building was shattered when the college occupied the several Lake Eden resort buildings. The Studies Building contained only rooms for classes and studies, and very little social contact, whereas every function of the college was carried on in the old Lee Hall, including meals and dormitories.

The resort buildings and their maintenance, the roads, the enlarged college farm, all required extra time and effort by faculty and students, for both shared in the business of maintaining the college. The ordinary chores now took on a scope adequate to the 700 new acres.

World War II brought yet another phase of development and new problems to the college. Much of the student body was drafted or volunteered for army duty. The college became, practically, a girl's school, and enrollment and financial aid dropped sharply. (Tuition was based on a sliding scale according to the student's ability to pay, and only the college treasurer knew who paid the full $1,200 and who paid less.) To counter this, the college initiated a series of summer institutes in the arts and music which proved an enormous success. Visiting artists such as Willem de Kooning, Ben Shahn, Robert Motherwell, Franz Kline, and Jean Charlot provided an important stimulus to the college. Charlot, an important figure behind the scenes of the first generation of Mexican art, was a summer teacher at BMC in 1944, and he painted two frescoes on concrete pylons supporting the Studies Building. They are still there, somewhat faded and bird-splattered, but the vitality of the artist and the early Mexican art movement is captured in the massive, blunt figures of "Tempest" and "Study." Other American artists received valuable and formative training while at Black Mountain, among them Kenneth Noland, a native of Asheville, and Robert Rauschenberg. Pop artist Rauschenberg, winner of the 1964 Venice Biennale, came to Black Mountain after reading an account of Josef Albers in a 1948 *Time* magazine which described Albers as the greatest art disciplinarian in the U.S. "I consider Albers the most important teacher I've ever had, and I'm sure he considers me one of his poorest students." Albers says he wasn't quite the poorest.

Through these summer institutes the college became a new center for American art and music, with composers such as Ernest Krenek, Stefan Wolpe, Lou Harrison, John Cage, and David Tudor as faculty members and visiting professors. Composer John Cage, with Merce Cunningham, M. C. Richards, and David Tudor, staged the first American "happening" at Black Mountain in 1962, and infuriated writer-critic Paul Goodman with his acerbic criticism of Beethoven in a summer lecture. (Actually, BMC faculty member and former Bauhaus instructor in theatre Xanti Schawinsky produced the first mixed media presentation at Black Mountain, in 1938, in an abstract theatre program. If a distinction between abstract theatre and a mixed media, unstructured happening is accepted, Schawinsky produced the first abstract theatre in America at BMC, and Cage, the first happening.)

But the problems brought on by the war were enormous, and financing became even more irregular and unsure in spite of the success of the summer programs. The ideal of retaining at least half of the previous year's faculty and students became unworkable under war circumstances. Ted Dreier, the college's long-time treasurer and one of the founders, commented in a summary report in 1949 that most of the faculty was exhausted by the strain of keeping the college together during the war years, and that new faculty members were not always aware of, or interested in, the founders' purposes and plans, but were intent on trying out their own pet ideas, rather than adhere to the original plan. Dreier remarked that they all seemed determined to repeat the errors Black Mountain had already survived. Although faculty members received no salaries, only room and board and a small sum for personal needs, from the first there was not enough money for BMC.

As a result of the war years' strain and financial difficulties, the original faculty group began to lose influence until, finally, the tension between old and new broke into a fight for the leadership in 1948. Dreier was ousted from his post as treasurer. The division between majority and minority factions the college had always sought to avoid was too great for reconciliation among some of the faculty. In 1949, Dreier, the Albers, Trudy Guermonprez, and Charlotte Schlesinger resigned their positions. As the core of the college's visual arts program, their leaving left the college without some of its sense of direction and conviction. Joseph Fiore took over as head of the arts

department until the college's end. Dreier's competent years as treasurer had kept the college financially afloat, even if precariously at times, and now with his leaving money became the ubiquitous, all-important concern.

Meanwhile, the college maintained its quality, but a new emphasis was inevitable without the Albers. The subsequent shift was from the visual arts to the literary arts. Out of this new and final phase came many of the foremost names in the new movement in poetry and prose in America. Names of contemporary poets such as Charles Olson, Robert Creeley, Joel Oppenheimer, Paul Blackburn, Robert Duncan, and Johnathan Williams were commonplace at Black Mountain, and their presence named a new group of poets. Kenneth Rexroth describes them in *Assays* as having laid the groundwork for "a new minor renaissance in American verse." The Black Mountain poets gravitated, when the college was disbanded, to the West and East coast urban centers, with the bulk going to San Francisco and Los Angeles. Rexroth, close to the Black Mountain group, served as a mentor-figure to some of the group. Allen Ginsberg, in an interview with Lawrence Lipton in 1956 (published *Holy Barbarians*, N.Y., 1969), said of the Black Mountaineers: "They're cool; having rejected everything they've become unable to utter anything except in the most roundabout way." Creeley was distinguished from the rest by Ginsberg because "he doesn't say anything except what he absolutely knows—simple—like on a basic, simple level, very short, epigrammatic, elliptical, like

> I went out.
> Got a beer.
> Ran into a milk truck,
>   by God.
> You won't understand me till you
> run into a milk truck.

The Black Mountain group takes its instruction from Ezra Pound and his formal theory and works to adapt it in the light of William Carlos Williams' concern with the idiosyncratically American manner and thought. And while these poets at first were known and admired only by a coterie, they have gained a position that is neither in the pantheon of "great poets" nor the obscure poet-mendicant responding alone to his "still, small voice." Although the Black Mountain poets haven't reached the point where high school English teachers sing their poetry like that of Byron and Keats, they have won a grudging respect or admiration from a literary elite whose poetic *weltschmerz* they set out to challenge.

The literary quarterly *Black Mountain Review*, which flourished under the editorship of Robert Creeley from 1954 to 1957, provided a first principal voice for many of today's best known poets, including Robert Duncan, Denise Levertov, Louis Zukofsky, Irving Layton, Paul Blackburn, and others. Creeley has said the quarterly's chief impetus was from Cid Corman's *Origin* which showed what a magazine was capable of "if it made its center the direct concerns in writing of those people who contributed to it. In that way, we felt a very distinct distance from the markedly literary-critical tone of so much writing of that period." In an article in *Serif,* from which the previous Creeley quote is taken, he comments, "it's odd to think that Black Mountain is now a label for the writers of that magazine, and that literary history to that extent defines us in a sense we neither had time nor interest to consider. No matter what such labels come to, I'm finally grateful for this one, just that it grants us our effect."

Finally, however, in 1956, the years of effort in trying to strengthen the college and prolong its life proved too much, and the faculty was forced to sell the last portions of its land and the college became Camp Rockmont for Boys. The end was brought about, legally, by the institution of legal proceedings to secure back salaries demanded by some faculty members. Under a complex and fatal system of "paper salaries," which had been carried on the books for years despite much pleading by Rector Charles Olson to have them written off annually, the college was suddenly not only bankrupt, but deeply in debt. Olson was appointed trustee for the college's assets and in 1962, the last of the debts was finally paid off, leaving Black Mountain's name clear at last. The papers of Black Mountain's life were transferred from an Asheville storage vault in 1963 to the North Carolina State Archives in Raleigh where they have finally been catalogued after several years' work.

As Robert Moore said in his foreword, "As an institution, Black Mountain College had ended, but its real life, the students and faculty, continue awaiting the judgment of time. Over the full range of its existence, Black Mountain College served as a remarkable stimulus to everyone involved, and acted as an unceasing guide to exploration . . . . The event of Black Mountain College is not yet over, and assessment of its complete significance lies in the future."

THE MAN WHO WRESTLED

By John Satterfield

When I wrote Bud that I was going to do a story about Lon Harlow, he answered, "Lon, my ruptured prostate! Try Jean. There's a ghost suitable for laying." Bud, like me, is a writer by nontrade; we've both put enough words on paper to know stories are not for pranging shadows. Or not only for that. Bud must have been beering when he composed his letter; his rhetoric leapt. "It's to *frame* that bloody night. However loosely, however crudely, you have to give it perspective and cover the windows so no rays of chaos can get in. Or out. I was lucky with Lon: I sublimated him in a surrogate tale—the one about that monstrous sheep castrater in the Sears catalogue. By the way, 'frame' is my aptest for the week. You frame Lon Harlow and you frame yourself. But have at it, Jack. What the hell else are we here for?" Punning, Bud doesn't choke on the most obvious because ambiguity at any level makes him feel sent. His word was apt. What we got to know about Lon came from other senses too, but when we saw him last the visual had the baton. A grisly picture it made. Bud has taken care of it in his way; I must now in mine.

"Hey, man, look at that hairdo."

"Where?" The Outdoors Inn was nearly full. I didn't know which way to look.

"Over by the table with the pine growing through it," Bud said. He upped his chin to point with the top of his head. In the gloom the hooded candles on the Inn's tables threw flickers seen from the bandstand. I shaded my eyes. At the tree-punctured table three little hurricane lamps made a rose glow around a man just sitting down. He pulled his chair forward, leaned on a forearm, and his face showed in the glow. The features ran together—he was forty feet away, and the lights on me from the bandstand ceiling were blinding—but the man had hair hanging below his ears.

"Holy mackerel!"

"*The* holy mackerel," Bud said.

I laughed and told him about my grandmother at the Passion Play. Right after I got my driving permit, she asked to go, and I was willing to take her; driving was new fun then. Nobody else in the family cared to give an evening to the Passion and miss Amos and Andy. It was over at last, a ramshackle show and poorly lit, and I led my grandmother around the tents to the field where we had parked. On the way I felt her arm tighten and heard her sharp sip of air. My eyes went where hers were staring, and I saw Jesus in nothing but his crown and loin cloth kissing a woman from the crowd—not very hard; he had his head pecking outward and was holding a hot dog in one hand and a Pepsi-Cola in the other. He spun from the girl to the weenie and pop, and he still had blood on the stigmatizing parts.

"Why—why, he's not supposed to do that!"

"What's he supposed to do, Granny?" My grandmother must have been too upset to answer.

Bud sucked quizzical dimples into his cheeks. "Is that the end? Your grandmother should say something like 'Listen, Clyde, don't be snotty with me.' Then she might reminisce about her great-uncle Henry." I was sneering at the kind of story he teased when Fay came up the stairs.

"Hey, did you guys—"

"Particularly if he grew up in India," Bud added.

Fay tried again. "Hey, *lis*ten. Did you guys see—"

"Afterthoughts make no points," I said to Bud. We both waited for Fay.

"Yeah, sugar," Bud said.

"Did you see that civilian out there with the long hair?" Fay was panting a little.

"Yes. Cute. Is he what made your eyes so wide?"

"Well, I don't know. He's some*body*. I mean, I recognize him, but I can't say who he is. I think he's a *movie* star."

"We thought he was from another type of drama," Bud said.

"Huh?"

"I'll explain it to you after the next set, Fay, baby," I said. "We've got to go." I beckoned to the rest of the band. They left the long table reserved for us and came onto the stand.

During our break, Bud and I had been changing a brass rhythm in an arrangement we wrote together, and he had suggested some tunes for the set coming up. I can't remember now what they were, except one. That one wouldn't be unusual—we had a good book—but Fay Maughn did it so well we could hardly play it. She was always the best, never failed to make even a routine tune a hair-raiser, but sometimes she was greater than the best, touching where scalding and chilling are the same. That night she took off on "Don't Worry 'bout Me." For me, it was one of the indelible times from the years of playing.

Bud had copied the melody from Chick Webb's

ALLIGATORS FOR TARZAN.

record. But Bud's arrangement, like him, floated on a plane that the Webb band as a whole never reached. Bud got into his arranging what Ella Fitzgerald got into her singing and what Taft Jordan got into his trumpet playing. Chick's arrangers never caught it, but Bud did; everything in his score leaned expectantly on the beat to come—it was going-somewhere music.

Then Fay's singing. It didn't come out of her head. She didn't think about it; she just did it. She neither practiced nor worked otherwise at singing, except to repeat words from lyrics—she had trouble memorizing them. But once heard, melodies were hers forever, and her ear always put pitches where Heifetz put them most of the time, where everybody knows they belong. Even more than melodic memory and good ear, the fresh fit of her phrases assured her sparkle. I never heard her do anything twice the same way, yet each choice she made seemed perfect when she made it. When Fay Maughn left us to join a certain clarinetist's orchestra (better, an uncertain clarinetist's; I can't remember his name—one way of telling the truth about his clarinet playing—but Benny Goodman, the musicians' grapevine said, called him an accordionist), MCA signed her and billed her as "The Girl with the 22-Karat Voice." The agency didn't say that her brain, too, was gold or some other solid, impervious to thought dents. Bud and I knew her limits, and so did most of the band. We didn't talk about them; we accepted them. Much better as singer than she could ever know, she was a simple natural. Wherever she went, Fay carried a suitcase packed with publicity men's glossy prints of actors and actresses, icons encouraging her on her pilgrimage to Hollywood. In her way, she made it; under the "Milestones" heading in a 1964 *Time*, the obit for Brona Scalder mentioned Fay, who disappeared with her in a chartered-plane crash. Miss Scalder, everyone knows, was crowding Doris Day for Number One. Until *Time*, with its usual taste, printed it, only a few knew that Fay's was the Scalder voice. For Fay Maughn of the magic talent and the dull head, it was all right to prefer celluloid shapes to people. All right and sad. Nasty prying *Time* knows better and cannot be forgiven: any near-Nazis who would climb J. D. Salinger's fence to find out how he works are trying to live psychological myths and dream reality. Screw Plato.

A doomed child, Fay, but not a villainess, she was

Illustrated by Mike Goins

hardly to be judged as wrong or right while she lived a fate she could not choose. But Fate, as if ashamed of Itself, gave her every freedom in singing, and none of us could hear her without being reminded that we more nearly normal ones might be free outside of music. Fay's singing cheered us when we were thinking of ourselves; when we thought of her, we were hurt.

Anything good on the bandstand we mostly heard over all kinds of crowd noise. Only rarely—maybe five or six times when I was present—did a crowd get quiet and stay quiet for a whole piece. Fay's "Don't Worry 'bout Me" shut everybody's mouth that night at the Outdoors Inn. It came fairly early in the evening, but what Fay did might have gotten through to everybody three drinking hours later—it was that good. Even the worst, the Lombardo lovers in the audience, couldn't miss it. Fay's voice embraced us; it shook us—gently, but we were jarred; it lifted us—where? For me, it was not a token but a call to the present, stating just its own worth, both nonarguing and vehement. It made me want to be nowhere else, at no other time, doing nothing other than catching ideas from her phrases and weaving them into the chords the piano part called for.

We didn't finish the set. "Don't Worry 'bout Me" was the third tune in it. I nodded to the band when it was over; they nodded back; we left the stand. I walked to the stockade-like fence where there was a dark spot. If I had to say why, I'd say it was to congratulate myself on being alive.

"Jack?" Jimmy Steele came up.

"Yeah, Jim."

"There's a man wants to talk to you, the one Bud says looks like Jesus. I saw him up close. He looks more like the last General Custer I saw in a horse opera, except his hair is dark. Boy, you should've seen the general in Shirley Temple ringlets. He was blonde —with an *e*. Sweet, man."

"Okay, Jim. Where's Bud?"

"Sitting behind the piano." Besides playing tenor, Bud was the band manager. He ought to be on hand in case Longlocks wanted to put us into the Meadowbrook, have us record for Columbia, or—more likely— ask us to play a charity ball at the country club in Tiffin, Ohio.

I stopped by the bandstand to say, "Come on, Bud. We may have a buyer out here."

He stood. "Fay got there, didn't she, Jack?"

"Beyond."

When we reached his table, Longlocks rose. Close, he didn't look at all like Sallman's portrait for Sunday Schools; he didn't look female. He was, however, so familiar that he was puzzling, and Bud and I exchanged a glanced question neither could answer. The man was shorter than either of us; he may have been five-six. His hair was long, but not to his shoulders. His ears showed, the slight waves pushed behind them. In other times and places he would not have

stood out, but in the summer of 1941 at a club built to bleed soldiers training at Camp Bookerman his hair and civvies set him apart. Uniforms were not required that summer, but they were cheaper to clean, and Bookerman people usually wore them.

"Lon Harlow," he said. We shook hands and sat down. "I'm a soft-drink man myself. What'll you have?"

"No time," I said. "It'd be good, but we have to play again in a few minutes."

"You guys turn out some terrific stuff."

"Thanks. Do you play?"

"No. Just follow jazz. Who's the one who plays those gutty trombone solos?"

"That's Jimmy Steele."

"Who writes for you?"

"We two do most of it," Bud said.

"Well, what are you two guys doing lost in the middle of North Carolina? You ought to be on the West Coast?"

Neither Bud nor I thought we were ready, but it wouldn't do to tell a potential buyer that. "We're sweating out the draft," I said.

"I'm 4-F." Harlow sat taller as if he were flexing his midriff.

"You look pretty healthy," Bud said.

"I am. As healthy as you can get. Except for one thing."

Bud and I often joked about predictable lines in conversations. This time he gave me a nod. I said, "Yeah? What's that?"

Harlow stuck a finger down the throat of a hurricane lamp. The flame split around his nail. "I feel the heat," he said. "I know my finger's hot. It doesn't hurt."

Bud was pulling his lips against his teeth so hard that his head was moving backward. "You mean you enjoy it?"

Harlow took his finger out. "I don't want to blister it. I have to use it in my work, and it might get infected." He looked at Bud. "I've heard of that kind. I'm not it."

"Well, wha—"

"All my pain nerves are dead. I feel touch, weight, movement, and all the rest of it—just no pain."

Maybe Harlow wanted to work the floor show, I thought, a little sick. I remembered a live ossified man being hit with a hammer in Ripley's Believe-It-or-Not Odditorium at the Chicago World's Fair. Worse, I recalled the fellow who popped an eyeball out of its socket to dangle by the optic nerve down his cheek. I hoped Harlow wasn't an act. "Feeling no pain must have its advantages."

"And disadvantages." He dropped his eyelids as if to read an evil list printed on their backs, then opened them. "The worst is I'm 4-F. Permanently."

Neither Bud nor I found words.

"That girl," Harlow said.

"Fay Maughn," we said together.

"She's got it." If he was talking about her singing, he was right.

Bud said, "The greatest," while I said, "The best."

"Could I meet her?"

"Sure," I said. "I'll bring her over after the next set."

The music didn't go well for me. Jimmy Steele brought off a fine "Out of Nowhere," but my head, on Lon Harlow, would not trim the vernier for its ears. I knew his face—but I could not put it in the right context. Losing a face that familiar is like forgetting who your brother is.

Fay was shining, a kid at a carnival gate, when I led her to Lon Harlow's table. She was pretty, so pretty it was uncanny. But whatever his desire, I didn't have to worry about Fay Maughn. She could take care of herself. Naturally most of us in the band—before pity for her unfired mind made us frigid with her—had tried her; we agreed she was soldered. We also agreed she meant it when she said she wasn't interested.

Harlow looked interested. When he stood, he was no taller than Fay. I was an intruder after introducing them, but curiosity killed my courtesy. "Several of us think we've seen you, but we can't say where. Can you?"

"Sure. In the movies."

Fay actually gasped. "Were you related to—"

Harlow laughed. "Oh, no. It wasn't her real name. It is mine. You haven't seen any billing for me because I don't get any. I'm a kind of stunt man. I wrestle alligators for Johnny Weismuller." Of course. Harlow's size had fooled us. He was a pocket Tarzan; the hair, the eyebrows, the mouth, the build—all were a proportionate reduction of Weismuller's.

"I thought they were just rubber lizards old Tarzan swished under water," I said.

"No. They're the goods in most scenes. They're not crocs. The scripts always call for crocs, but they're alligators. We shoot the scenes in Silver Springs."

"Does the whole company leave Hollywood and go on location in Florida?" Breathless Fay spoke her fan-magazine vocabulary. She probably thought the little camera crew for the Florida shots had to have a commissary and a grip.

"No. Funny thing. I've never met Weismuller. His jungle is in L. A. They shoot his underwater stuff in a tank. Except for what I do for him in Silver Springs."

"What happened to the pain nerves?" I wish I could draw a less obnoxious character for myself—until I remember we're all bastards.

Harlow was able to turn his frown into a short laugh.

"What pain nerves?" Fay asked.

Harlow told her. I was glad he didn't demonstrate again. Then he said, "I work—did work until I quit to take my job at Bookerman—at the Ross Allen Reptile Institute. I was bitten."

Fay looked at me. "Rattlesnakes," I said to her.

Harlow nodded. "The first time it happened, I was late getting the antidote. The doctors said I almost died. The next five or six times, I got the serum early enough, but somewhere along there my pain receptors dimmed out. And eventually they stopped working altogether. One compensation: I'm immune to rattlesnake venom. Before I left to come to Camp Bookerman, I gave some doctors several pints of blood to see what they could find out about antibodies."

Fay was charmed. Harlow might have been a great head-weaving snake himself; she could hardly blink in her gaze at him. I wasn't charmed. The whole story put a lump in my esophagus. It ached like conscience for some future guilt.

He tilted his forehead to compliment Fay's singing, and he smiled. He had looked just as warmly at Bud and me, but the angle now was new, and the lamps glistened on the chrome-bright squares of his teeth. So large, regular, white, I thought, that they might be cosmetic dentistry. I excused myself from the table —I wasn't going to loose my curiosity on *them*.

Bud came with me up the stairs to the stand. We should have selected numbers, but I told him about the pain nerves and the rattlesnakes. The story didn't go well with him. The lifting of his left cheek toward his eye was his expression of sympathy, the hurt he always took before the idea of a malfunctioning man. And he paled enough to make me guess he was queasy. He sat down in the sax row. "My mouth's so dry I can't wet my reed. Instead of calling a set, ask Jimmy to play with just the rhythm section." His careful, matter-of-fact tone surely covered a plea.

I leaned out to the band's table to say Jimmy Steele and the rhythm would go for a while. Everybody walked onto the stand anyhow. It was that kind of band. But even more, Jimmy Steele (we were a body good enough to avoid a pecking order, but he was our unbending goad and chief gift-bearer) was that kind of trombonist.

Twenty-some minutes later we left the bandstand. I said to Bud, "Okay?"

"Now, yes. How about you?"

"What do you mean?"

"You were green when you told me about Harlow. I thought you were going to faint."

"Oh." I hadn't hidden anything; maybe he could have wet his reed. "I'm okay now."

That twenty-some minutes was distance for down-setting stomachs. But they were special minutes, as were any filled by Jimmy Steele's trombone. I'm sure words are futile at reproducing music. Others aren't sure. Jimmy Steele's playing defeats all arguments of the others. A couple of weeks after the Outdoors Inn, we cut some lo-fi seventy-eights at a Tinker Toy radio station in Waycross, Georgia. When Bud and I met recently, we taped the Jimmy Steele solos from them for the folk-music archives at the Library of Congress. Some knowing critic—aren't they all?—will write that Jimmy Steele was post-Teagarden and pre-Harris. Categories will swarm on him like vampire bats on a lost lamb—late hot, early cool, neo-swing, precursory or inchoate bop. Blind bats, they will have jumped a unique white cat with veins of diamond, one who always knew where he was. Purring or roaring, he says so clearly, "I am Jimmy Steele," that all categories fall from him thirsty and bloodless, dead shapes he'd not take time to scorn. If everybody were as much himself as Jimmy Steele was what he was, we'd all be men; nobody would be a critic and vice versa.

Earlier I said that with beer Bud's rhetoric leapt; fraught, mine has just sagged—three beers didn't lift it. By temperamental choice we both are gross with the unsayable, leaving the net sayable to logicians. (I'm obviously not, subjectively or objectively, beyond criticism. I'm not a Jimmy Steele. Mostly I must be a drained Dracula. Otherwise something would reflect me and show I'm real.)

Jimmy's twenty-some minutes of trombone gave us heart to finish the evening. When we quit after two o'clock, I was beat. Then I had to spend time finding my plump promised waitress and saying, "Not tonight." She was tired too, but she smiled for tomorrow and called me Victor Manure. Her sister's name for Bud was Humphrey Gofart. The girls struck back at their mother for the Theda and Pola she had stuck them with. They were as healthy and obscene as any wish. Talk is what they did mainly—before, after, even during—so they progressed from Bud's Twa to Twatt to Twaddle to Prattle to Babble-lay Sisters. They had the answer for almost everything.

At our cabin Bud was already out of the shower. "Didn't you have a date?"

"Did," he said. "Don't. Too sleepy." He got into his bed.

I was slow undressing and long under the water. Fay's flight ("Don't Worry 'bout Me"), Lon Harlow's story, Jimmy Steele's trombone—too raw, too true, too much for one night. My towel was dragging. Outside the bath, the light was off; I supposed Bud was asleep. In the dark I felt along the wall to my bed and fell on it limp as the towel I'd dropped on the tile. For a moment Harlow's face was a fresco on the ceiling— until I closed by eyes. That ceiling was dry long before Lon Harlow appeared; into my damp brain he was permanently applied.

"Didn't you?" Bud's voice reached into the dark.

"Didn't I what?"

"Have a date."

"Tomorrow."

"I hope it'll be there." No need to ask whether Bud's "it" referred to tomorrow or to Theda. He meant both and more. Probably he was lying across the room overwhelmed, thinking this is what happens when you fool around with all that jazz.

About three days later, Fay told us at lunch (eggs and sausage are "lunch"—to keep time square) more about Lon Harlow. "He's a physical-training instructor at Camp Bookerman. He teaches swimming, and all the men have to learn how to keep a life preserver from breaking their arms when they jump off a ship. Lon takes them up a forty-foot tower and asks them to jump."

"Into water?" Bud asked.

Fay's "Um-m-m" was in her yes nod, her eyes watching her busy fork. I learned far back to scowl past her profile at Bud, but my lips twitched. Her mouth formed an o for her fork, then turned the shape to sound. "Oh, Bud. Of course." She laughed; so we could.

"Is that all he does?"

"Yes, here—I mean, at Bookerman. But he's been on leave twice to go to Florida and make some scenes for Tarzan pictures. Boy, he's serious about those movies. He's studied all the Tarzan books—just to fight alligators. He could do a lot better."

"What?" I asked.

"His stepfather is a big, big producer. Lon could be a star."

"Why isn't he?"

"He says his stepfather can't help him. I wish Lon would listen to reason." Meaning herself, who had none. Fay stuck her chin out all the time. Neither Bud nor I would clip it.

Bud said, "Maybe Harlow's doing something nobody else can do. I sure as hell won't wrestle an alligator, and I'll bet Johnny Weismuller won't."

"Oh, but, Bud, Johnny Weismuller is somebody." Bud winced and I grinned. "Lon Harlow doesn't have to be just an alligator wrestler."

On the way out of me my impulse to be preachy bumped head-on into what I knew about Fay. Across the table I could almost see words forming over Bud's head, words about cruelty and naïveté. He wouldn't say them. But Fay shouldn't look down on Harlow because of his work; he wasn't a garbage man.

Our brief silence exhausted Fay's span of attention. "Hey, I want to show you guys something." She rummaged in her enormous pocketbook that we'd heard a Bookerman soldier call a footlocker. "Not it, but I don't—no—I haven't shown you this, have I?" We passed around a card with Dorothy Lamour's signature. Fay kept digging. "I got that when she came to Raleigh selling defense bonds." Her eyes were helping her hand in the purse, so Bud could shake his head at her autograph hounding and hero worshiping. "I can't find it. Must have left it in my cabin. It's a letter from the man who manages—"

Fay finished the sentence; I can't because I don't remember that clarinet player's name. My head dipped to tell Bud to say the line Fay had cued.

"What'd it say?"

"He asked me to send some records and pictures. It's a kind of audition, I guess."

"Are you going to?"

"It won't hurt anything. I won't make it." Fay worked at getting her pocketbook closed, and when she looked up at us, she was startled, then puzzled, then—

finally—aware. She blushed. "Aw, I don't *want* to leave you guys. *Ever.* Good gosh, Bud and Jack and Jimmy Steele, Snake and Killer and everybody. I don't *want* to."

"Then don't think about it." Bud made it harsh, but blushed himself, changed to normal tone, asked, "Did Harlow behave okay?"

"Do you *mean*—"

"What else?"

"Sure, he behaved. The third night—*last* night—he kissed me. It was *weird.* He just held me close with his arms still, and his lips—well, they didn't *move,* I mean, he doesn't know how to—shucks, it's the way a *cous*in kisses. That's all. He didn't *try* anything. Why?"

If Bud had what I had in mind, he wouldn't tell her. "Just want to be sure you're okay."

"Lon Harlow is a *real* gentleman."

"Naturally. He's a Greystoke."

"What's that?" Fay asked me.

I was laughing at Bud's absurd memory when I told her. "Tarzan was from British aristocracy, from Lord and Lady Greystoke. He inherited the lordship himself. He just *happ*ened to grow up among apes. He didn't have to become one, for heaven's sake, unless he chose to."

"Oh." Fay got the facts anyhow. "Well, Lon *is* a gentleman. I told him he ought to look more like a *movie* personality. He dresses like a businessman. He could be some*body.*"

Our silence must have said something to Fay. When she spoke again it was a little sharply. "*My* date is nice. That's more than I can say for that Theda and Pola. Why, Pola told me a joke *full* of the *fil*thiest words I ever heard, and it wasn't *fun*ny. It didn't have any *point.*"

Bud and I didn't turn to one another. The telepathy was clicking, "No point! Theda and Pola have the finest repertory in North Carolina. Poor Fay, you don't get them."

"Why do you guys fool around with those girls?"

"They're our pair o' doxies," Bud said. He had sprung that on me before, but I wasn't ready for Fay's question.

"What are doxies?"

"Bud was using Latin for 'outlaws,'" I tried. "In the scenes we're making with Theda and Pola, he's William S. Hart and I'm Tom Mix."

"You guys are nuts. Then how come they call you Victor and Humphrey?"

"Aw," Bud said, "those girls are always twisting their tales."

"*Bud!* You're awful."

"I'm sorry." His face showed he did regret under-shooting her. "It was a bum joke." With *that* corny little difference, he overshot her. Fay accepted his apology!

"Okay. I'll see you guys later—I want to find that *thing.*" She left us to look for her letter from the clarinetist's manager.

The way Bud brought his coffee cup to his lips about three quick times told me he was arguing with himself over whether to say something. I kept changing the angle of my knife and fork on my plate. Then he started to speak slowly, as if he were having to prod himself. "That still-lipped kiss now. Do you suppose—uh—that when Harlow lost his pain nerves he also lost his ability to—"

"Man, that's the question I was hoping I wouldn't—I mean, you wouldn't ask." I guess he saw in my eyes what I saw in his, because he dropped the subject.

"Poor Fay. She's really out of it, isn't she, Jack?"

"Yes, but she's out of danger too."

"Wonder which joke that lunatic Pola told her."

Remembering the possibilities, we laughed.

Lon Harlow's second act began that night with his entrance. After twelve o'clock, we saw him in a sky-blue seersucker jacket. The males at the tables of the Outdoors Inn were in summer Army uniforms, their women's colors splashing the tan background. Lon's blazer drew some stares when he came in and sat down.

"Now, that's more *like* it," Fay said. I had to swallow a bitter word. Fay had just asked that we finish the set with a substitute for "Sophisticated Lady"—I'd called the Ellington tune—so she was pushing my patience with her remark about Lon's clothes. I wished she'd not be compulsive about what he wore. And I wished she had not forgotten the words to "Sophisticated Lady."

Bud didn't make it any easier for Fay to remember. He sang frequent parodies that seemed to go with pop melodies better than the published lyrics did. We—the band—loved Bud's improvised words, but they were disastrous for Fay. Once she started her second chorus of "Amapola" into the mike with Bud's version:

Panacea,
You give me diarrhea.

Embouchures faulted into guffaws, and Jimmy Steele (he could somehow buzz the center of his lips with the corners stretched in a grin) had to finish the chorus in a raucous line that was a musical parody of Bud's poem—accompanied only by a shaking rhythm section, the arrangement turned to unscored whoops by the horn blowers. Fay sat down like a spent rose, and for a long time through our laughs we did not see her tears.

"Sophisticated Lady" I meant to hear, so at the end of the set, when Fay and Bud started toward Lon Harlow's table, I went to our cabin to copy the words. Even if late starting again, we were going to play "Sophisticated Lady." On the lacquered veneer of the dresser was the portable phonograph Bud and I had bought on halves. Besides the Gideon Bible, our books were there, my *Gargantua and Pantagruel* and Bud's collected Keats. In the short times we had for reading, we exchanged them. One dawn when we came in from bedding Theda and Pola for the night, we were at the books a little while before sleeping. Bud said over his volume of verses, "This cat is earthier than Rabelais. How the hell do you unravish a bride?" It was a wilder image than Gargantua's horse flooding three or forty counties.

Bud's records were—generally—on one side of the phonograph, mine on the other. I was going to leaf through my stack when I saw his Duke Ellington album on top of his pile. In the big white space on it, Mr. Ellington had signed it for Bud, the *D* as huge as an equator seen from a pole, the rest of the autograph a jagged scar on the surface. Mr. Ellington wrote his name so much the same each time that I wouldn't be able to tell which album was mine if I found the other one. I used Bud's. I was sure he cared no more than I which was which. I wrote the words while "Sophis-ticated Lady" was playing and took them back to the bandstand.

Bud was waiting there. While we picked numbers to go with "Sophisticated Lady," Bud told me that Harlow had combed all of Fayetteville to find the azure jacket. Excited as always by the sharp, Bud spoke to me fast: he had said Harlow in blue looked like a painting by Turner, and Harlow had corrected him with, "You mean Gainsborough."

"He said he has a Dartmouth degree—and he's a stunt man. I believe him. Nobody could invent that combination. He enjoys the humor of it. When Fay went out to nose her powder, Harlow said he'd bought the jacket to please her, to look Hollywood. He said something curious too, that all you could do for Fay was go along with her picture of things, that it couldn't be changed. And he said, 'It's too bad about her, isn't it? But maybe it isn't. She can be happy without questions, and most of us can't be happy without them and are miserable with them—unless we find that asking itself is fun.' How about a philosopher who wrestles alligators?"

"The jaws of the dilemma."

"I like the old horny metaphor. It's better for all that bull."

We played our set, "Sophisticated Lady" in it, and Bud and I went with Fay to Lon Harlow's table. I wanted to know whether anybody at Dartmouth played jazz, but I didn't get a chance to ask. Harlow had been joined by a corporal named Knowland Leach. From Harlow's clear consonants, outlandish to my Southern ears, I got the Knowland. If I hadn't been there and Bud or Jimmy Steele had heard it and told me, I'd have spelled it Nolan. I've never met a Noland. The name Knowland sticks because with it Harlow maybe accidentally primed the pump of events. They were to flood.

Both got up, the corporal slowly, his way of showing us we were interrupting, and Harlow introduced us. "Corporal Knowland Leach."

"Buster," the corporal said, louder and quicker than a welcome to familiarity. It signaled that his Christian name was a sore. Buster Leach, from about six-five, stared over my head and Bud's without recognition. The hand he jutted out looked as stiff-angled as his chevrons, but it felt both rough and limp. At Fay, his eyes dropped; she was especially pretty that night with the tan on her throat pinked above the single-rose corsage Harlow had brought her. Buster seemed to be measuring her, but coldly. He moved his heavy gaze back to Harlow. "So I just looked at yer papers at headquarters ter find out."

"Let's sit." Harlow said to Fay, " 'Sophisticated Lady' was fine. I didn't know—"

"I found out plenty," Buster said.

"Nothing that would interest these people, corporal." It came out gently, and Harlow turned toward Fay. "I've never heard words to that—"

"Hell it won't. Yer file is so screwy anybody'd be interested. Like that college mess—Darthmouth and all. What's a interlectural like you doing teaching PT? With all them honors you oughter be big dog at West Point—*if* you was a sojer."

Calm, Harlow explained to us. "Knowland and I do the same kind of work at Bookerman. He's the head GI instructor in PT, and I'm the only civilian on his staff. He has something he wants to talk to me about, but this is not the time." To Buster he said, "Tomorrow. At the Camp, Knowland."

"Buster!"

"All right. Buster. Tomorrow." Harlow was as polite as if the big man hadn't yelled at him. Bud and I leaned forward, ready to distract Buster, but Harlow raised his palm toward us. He had to take care of Bookerman people in his own way.

"You dint have ter take yer job at Camp. You just have ter be around men, huh?"

Harlow's palm held toward her didn't stop Fay. "Listen, Buster, Lon's my *date*. He's a real *gentleman*."

Harlow smiled. Not a passive smile, it became a laugh. "A gentleman who wrestles alligators."

"I read that in yer papers too." Buster saw nothing funny. "And about yer pain nerves."

"Fill the form and your life story is public property." Harlow laughed again at that—he laughed with joy; anybody else in his place might have laughed, but nervously. "The form and what's in it tell the truth."

"Maybe that frilly jacket yer wearing tells the truth."

Listen, Buster. I told him to get one like it. *I* like it. Fay could not draw Buster's attention.

"I don't wanter see my men in no fancypants outfits. They oughter look like men." It was peremptory and for Harlow. "I *do* wanter see that about the pain nerves fer myself." His long hand jumped to Harlow's shoulder.

"Buster," Fay said, "don't *start* anything. I told you Lon's a *gentleman*."

Lon's eyes moved to Fay while the great hand moved to his ear. He kept looking at her unblinking as Buster's thumb and index finger closed on the lobe. Bud and I leaned again, and Harlow's palm came up enough to stop us. We could not help; we could only watch and wait. Buster's knuckles grew taut and trembled, the effort shivering up his arm, through his shoulder, into his thick torso. Harlow did nothing but look at Fay. Buster grunted the last ounce of pressure into his pincers and dropped them to the table. Disbelief was on his face. The lobe of Harlow's ear was dead white for about three seconds, then brightened scarlet that bruised toward blue.

"I hope you're *satisfied*, Buster. You *can't* start anything with Lon." Fay said it as if *she* were defeating Buster.

Buster was baffled. Where his tan skin met sleeves and collar, there was no shift of hue. His hair and brows were the chino shade of his uniform. Even his eyes, small and with no white showing, were light brown; against his clothes and skin and hair they were colorless. I knew Bud would see the incongruity: an angry military man rendered in a perfectly neutral tone.

Baffled, Buster was not satisfied. "Loan me yer pin," he said to Fay.

"What for? *No!*"

"It's all right. Let him have it," Harlow said. We could see his pulse—it was not fast—in the bluing bottom of his ear.

"Lon, you're not going to *start* anything?"

"No. Finish something." He smiled his too-nice teeth into view. "Let Knowland—let Buster have it."

Fay undid her rose. Buster took the long pin with the round head—to me it shone as big as a tenpenny nail—and looked at Harlow.

"Hold it in the candle first. I can't afford an infection." Harlow was directing Buster.

The pin blackened, then glowed in the flame. Buster lifted it, eager, and said, "Where?"

Harlow laid the middle finger of his right hand on the tablecloth. "It's on its side. Go through the ball, but don't scratch the bone." A third time he had raised a palm toward Bud and me. Already we were leaning backward, away from what we saw. Under Buster's push, the pin went through the finger and into the table. Buster wrenched it out. A drop of blood welled; then Harlow popped his finger into his mouth while his left hand reached for a handkerchief. I heard my teeth grit and saw Bud's jaw clench.

"Maybe yer kidding me," Buster said. He was tense, excited, somehow much taller. "Maybe it's not that way all over yer body." After sucking it a moment, Harlow had wiped his finger. He folded his handkerchief and pushed back the left side of the blue jacket to get at his hip pocket. Buster's hand jerked as if shot from a coil, then came back. The pinhead stuck tacked to the front of Harlow's shirt, just above his belt and below his ribs. He glanced down at the red stain inking as his shirt blotted, and he plucked out the pin.

"It won't show with my jacket buttoned," he said to Fay. He was apologizing to her!

Buster had shrunk, his head dangling to the side. He cleared away some phlegm and said, "When I'm ready agin, I'm going ter fix you so you'll know yer fixed." All intent on Harlow, we didn't notice when Buster slid away.

Bud said, "Are you okay?"

Harlow said, "Yes."

"Why'd you do it?"

"I have to do my job at Bookerman. He could ruin it for me. It's the only way I can fight."

Fay was white, then red as Harlow's ear before it turned blue-black. "You could beat him, Lon."

He laughed. "Fay, you really take movies seriously, don't you? I mean, you think they are true. Look, I'm a lightweight. Leach has at least forty pounds on me. He could crush me, 'fix' me, as he said. The little good guy can't always whip the big bad guy—if there are, outside of movies, good guys and bad guys."

Fay didn't believe him, only in him. "You could beat him, Lon."

Harlow's eyelids came down slowly, as if he saw now how hooded Fay's vision was; I thought he might let the sad reflection linger on his face, but he changed it. "It's over for tonight. Say, isn't it time for you to play?"

The groan was mine or Bud's or a mixture. On the way to the bandstand Bud said, "Get Jimmy to play. I can't right now."

Jimmy Steele called solo in a few bars that spelled the key and invoked the trio in the rhythm section. Then we joined his middle-paced tempo for some blues. I know: the form harks back and the manner must be fresh. But Jimmy Steele neither appealed to tradition nor urged the future. He told what no word-monger can accept as music's message: music. The only possible symbolic literation of it is "Now." Jimmy Steele wound up the evening for us. Bud and I should have been the ones to thank him; the rest of the band had not seen the bruise and the blood at Lon Harlow's table, and they didn't need Jimmy as Bud and I needed him. But it was they who thanked him, mostly with good-natured jeers: "He can't play in tune but he does get a lousy tone"; "What do I think of his execution? I'm in favor of it." We recognized that Jimmy Steele had more craft than we. Nobody in the band felt jealousy toward him—jealousy is supposed to be among the ubiquitous and immortal things.

After we had stored the music and instruments, I began looking for Theda. The Outdoors Inn was crowded as always, and it took a weary time to find her. I told her I was sorry but I couldn't go off with her. She said, "Okay, Vic, if that's the way you don't want it."

Showered already, Bud was standing by his bed when I got to the cabin. I repeated what Theda had said, and he tried to grin. "You broke your date with Pola?" I asked.

"Yes."

"How'd she take it?"

"I don't know exactly. You might say she gave me an enematic smile."

I knew he was tired. "Oh, no, Bud, *you* might say it."

"Right now I'd have to have the strength of a lion to manage a sheepish expression. Cut out the light when you go to the bathroom, will you?" He sagged onto his bed.

I undressed and flicked the switch. Before I could turn on the light in the bath, I tripped over the soggy towel Bud had dropped there. It was by a pair of my socks he'd worn without asking—are the most thoughtful also the most thoughtless? I tried the water cold; I tried it hot. I wanted sleep; I was awake. When I lay down, that livid fresco on my cranium's ceiling looked back at me, the black lobe of its ear throbbing. Lon Harlow would stay there whether I slept or not. Since that night I've laughed every time I've read the pious, poker-faced lie that somebody "single-mindedly devotes all his waking hours to" something. My God, what about double-mindedly? What about sleeping hours? I was back at Harlow's table, watching the pin go through his finger and into his middle. Then I was at Ripley's Believe-It-or-Not Odditorium in Chicago, seeing a man with a saucer-sized hole clean through his abdomen and an attendant who ran a sword back and forth into the belly and out the back. People paid for seeing things like that. I don't know whether I was awake or asleep when the shakes started, but I had them. Bad. I was trembling worse than Guy Lombardo's sax section.

Bud's voice probed the darkness. "That Buster Leach is a son of a bitch. He probably would visit a hospital so he could laugh at sick people and cripples."

I was glad he was awake; talking to him might be better than quaking alone. "Right. He's about as absolutely what he is as anybody could be."

"Wonder if there's any absolution for the absolute." Abstraction fascinated Bud, and he hated it. Its poisonous vacuums he rattled with the bite of his wit. At our best, we can borrow from each other the courage to laugh; we were not at our best. "I'm scared, Jack. Harlow does exactly what Buster wants."

In the dark I worked to keep my voice steady. "And, Bud, he does exactly what Fay wants. She's not a bitch."

"No, she's not. But Harlow evidently believes he must do what both Buster and Fay expect. That's what scares me."

He didn't say more. Maybe he was asleep, maybe fighting his own shakes. I didn't feel very good, quivering with Lon Harlow wrought over my brainpan. I surely didn't feel like any Victor. Theda should have called me Jack Lament.

The afternoon about three days later was cool enough for softball. In an opening bordered by trees we played a supple game. The sky, the woods, the fast young bodies, the shouts touched Bud. "It's pretty, man. If Keats had seen this lark, he'd have said 'lithe spirit.' Wow! It is pretty."

"You know it."

We watched Jimmy fly out to center field, then said laughing to one another, "How do we know it?"

Bud aped a professor who had had us at the University, "Not without application here is the doctrine of universal consent." (To explain a private joke I shared with Bud, I have to worry about an inside narrative.) Professor Roberts was a composite of all the ineffective teachers he had seen in movies. Mostly he gave us what we'd never use, facts about obsolete forms. Superlatives, litotes, and sarcasm—he called it irony—so garbled his argument—he called it debate—that everybody had to guess what he was thinking. When I said Schubert was hardly out of the running for the schmaltziest, Professor Roberts said, "I'm most uncertain, Mr. Lamont, whether we mightn't be pursuing the vaguest, sheerest phantom in your word 'schmaltz.'" Once this negative machine told us we could learn no mean truths from positivists. Bud had naturally seconded my notion on Schubert's schmaltz, and Professor Roberts had ruled him out of order. "Now, Mr. Cranbury, I must tell you and your friend Mr. Lamont, you gentlemen, in the kindest way possible, that it is not in the least unlikely that your strongest points will be defeated by *the doctrine of universal consent*. Wouldn't it be nearest the truth, Mr. Cranbury, to say that you listen in a manner not dissimilar to that of everyone else?" Bud said he heard with his own ears. "Oh, come now, Mr. Cranbury, aren't you perhaps taking this not altogether impersonally?" Bud grinned and said he didn't mind listening to music personally. Professor Roberts didn't grin. I hoped he was hurting. That was not the littlest hole Bud had ripped through him. Bud grinned again when I told him he had bested the professor.

I use the softball game as a diversion. First, I digress for selfish reasons, stalling off what I have to tell about Lon Harlow. I have to tell it, but I don't have to dig it because it's right on the surface. I must, however, turn every stone lying there. Under each rock I see a slick classicist or a fundamentalist or some other ismy slitherer. The slippery things delay me. Categorically. But I digress also for formal reasons—that is, as well as for informality. Between Lon's first and second acts with musicians on the stage or in the pit, Bud and I had a happy lunch with Fay. Before Lon's final act, we play ball with other virgins. Naïve women connect the lunch and the game into a pure intermezzo of fun, like *La serva padrona—entr'acte* fare relieving three-act classic opera; frustrated translators call it *The Maid as Mistress*.

The "show" at the Outdoors Inn was the Llewellyn School of the Dance—little experience, little fee—from Birmingham. Llewellyn itself, with pointed shoes and the first name Donny, rehearsed and directed, a shrill caricature, enough theta in its sigma to double Bud and the other saxes behind their stands. "Girls, *girls!* It's not just a matter of *hav*ing a personality; it's a matter of pro*ject*ing it, a matter of *sell*ing it." He wore an odd cologne. Heartsease probably. Privately, Llewellyn seemed as male as anybody. He told Bud and me that getting students was tough, that he had had to draw his covey of young quail from their leery mothers. So publicly, he was a dancing master straight out of he movies. He had some reputation—he had performed in Vitaphone shorts—but Bud said Llewellyn's fruit act was the real decoy.

The chorus was a line of twelve Alabama pullets bred for meaty breasts, but they were for on-foot window-shopping, not for plucking. A thwarting arithmetic gave the twelve about forty mothers chaperoning. Those ageless bloodsuckers automatically phalanxed all soldiers away. We musicians—not much older than the girls, most of us had finished in June our third year at the University—were more suspect than the soldiers. The mothers, superstitious as everybody else about musicians, thought we were only interested in playing, sex, and bawdy stories; two of every three musicians were sure roués, if not rapists. Always under the mothers' eyes, the closest we got to the girls was in a softball game like this one. We could enjoy their grace between awkward plays.

The sounds were pungent: the lush tock of the bat on the ball, sneakers squeaking on a turn where the parking pavement faceted the diamond, the girls' shorts sizzling as they ran. Bud, bantering the national pastime and unable to keep his eye on the ball, hummed "America the Beautiful," singing an occasional word like "beautiful."

It was beautiful. The girls in their print blouses, we in white undershirts, all of us brown and moving, the game fitted in that field edged by straight trees, belonged. The sky *was* spacious—unmarked and Carolina blue, lighter than Aegean blue. The tall pines stood green and bold against it. A Carolinian looking up past his needling tree can see as far as any Greek sighting along a mathematically fluted column.

The beauty was both urgent and relaxed, both fresh and timeless. Particularly against the OD of the military convoy making the serpentine curve around the Outdoors Inn. The drab paint of those vehicles was protective! Seeing it from our bright game, I thought the Army must be color-blind. Maybe it believed everybody was stupid enough to confuse camouflaged appearances and the actual goods.

Bud sang "amber waves" to a Goldilocks in the chorus, hummed, sang, "I love my rocks and rills, thy woods and templed hills." Once when we both chased a hot bouncer into left field, he said, "No world is made of continents." I was shocked. Not because it was as old pun; he ranges widely between good and bad. But in the context—we amateurs didn't care about sharp lines between infield and outfield, now

who was on what team; we were having a fine time, girls on the diamond, all of us yelling at one another the language at once most idiomatic and most universal, like "lemme have at ol apple" and "batter up" and "attababy"—in that context, what Bud said was relevant and desperate.

Jimmy Steele, who knew better than most how the world was made, dated the mothers; he said they were batting .667. Young musicians should have the statistics as a warning. Or as a clue.

When the shadows grew long, we called our outing, and Bud and I went to our cabin. We showered for the dinner session. In our maroon jackets without lapels we'd look like the men in the name bands that had played Chapel Hill that year. We had seen such jackets on orchestras in recent musical films, and Bud had found ours through an ad in *Downbeat*. They stood out like inflamed goiters among the khaki uniforms at the Outdoors Inn. "Khaki"—didn't Bud wear that out! He exploited both our Southern "cacky" and the overheard Yankee "cocky"—as broad *a*'s are worked. Phonetically.

Fay knocked at our door. She brought in a wire from the manager of that clarinet player I can't remember. He wanted her in October, when the clarinetist would take his band into Roseland. (He also wanted to change Maughn to Vaughn, as if that had some commercial significance.) The records and pictures she had mailed him sold her. Cruel Fay was blindly happy. She probably couldn't see the pained glances Bud and I traded. We'd not cross her; we'd not complain; we'd hide our feelings of loss. We congratulated her, acting our joy in her success. It was a scene from all the tasteless Hollywood musicals, but we played it well. We didn't overdo it. When she ran out to tell the others, Bud broke the button off of his shirt collar and I lost a lyre-shaped cuff link down the commode.

That night, Lon Harlow appeared at the Outdoors Inn wearing rope-soled loafers of navy denim and a fancy pink slack suit. On the bandstand, I heard his entrance before I saw it. It was a sudden hush between numbers—the click of stainless steel stopped with the clack of small talk; several hyena laughs and some loud snorts twisted my head toward the tables. There stood Lon, nodding to Fay before he sat down. She said, "I drove to Raleigh with him Wednesday and picked out that suit for him. I've got a picture of Errol Flynn in one just *like* it." I almost said something ironic about her Little Lord Fauntleroy, but swallowed it—ridiculous words: I contained myself.

After the last show by the Llewellyns, we were, as usual, to play about forty minutes. The vocal for Fay was "You Stepped out of a Dream." Jimmy Steele took the first chorus, his trombone a torch leading us into that special stretch of self which renews tired players and makes them superior, and Fay began. She sang the title line with a glorious quality, and then she stopped. Words forgotten? My racing anger glared an oven at her. "O-o-o-oh" descended through the speakers—she had not forgotten; she was scared songless, looking toward the dance floor.

Buster Leach was there. The halves of Harlow's ripped pink jacket flagged in Buster's hands. That khaki face scowled across them and across three concrete yards at Harlow. Peeled to the waist, Lon stood by his table, his swimmer's muscles shimmering in the candlelight. Suddenly we were not playing any more. A second silence spread like a plague through the Outdoors Inn as everyone boiled to his feet. Present emphatic tension does twinkle with contagion; exposed to the stars, the Outdoors Inn must suffer the universal disease. Soldiers had always broken up scuffles among themselves; they wanted the Inn on limits. Until now, we had not had a soldier tackle a civilian, and uniform witness would call the soldier right. The crowd waited.

Buster screeched, "I said no more of yer pantywaist outfits. You probly got lace on yer drawers."

Still the crowd kept quiet. Harlow answered, "All right, Knowland," and turned to walk toward the exit. The soldiers who filed to block him were as precise as if choreographed. They came, about twelve of them, from tables near Lon's, closed the aisle, and surrounded him. We heard their shoes on the cement and the rustle of their clothes; they did not speak.

Buster shouted, "Turn im loose. He's mine." Above the soldiers' huddle, Lon's pink pants fluttered in an uplifted hand, and hoots broke out in the audience.

I went forward. Shiny maroon moving in the corner of my eye told me Bud and the other saxes were stepping around their stands. I knew—because I knew them and could hear—the brass and rhythm were behind us. We got to the edge of the bandstand, and a minor bit happened—unprepared, coincidental, and the only incredible part of what I have to tell about Lon Harlow. A short-maned woman in breeches of onager shade and shape pranced toward Buster, her platform soles thumping like hoofs on the concrete. Her horse face appalled, with no reverence for the serious act she both announced and parodied, she pointed to us and brayed, "The redcoats is coming!" Buster was surprised—by her, not by us, we knew a few steps later—and he waved her on. As all of us jumped off the bandstand, I recognized choreography again: the minute men at the tables on the sides of the dance floor saw us, they rushed out, three for every one of us; they grabbed us, one to an arm, an extra behind each of us. Clearly, Buster Leach had known we would have to be held, and his troops were ready. He evidently had not known that woman would trot on stage. As uncomfortable as I am about her intruding in the story—at the time she seemed more than real—I am more uncomfortable remembering that she cast us musicians, for Christ's sake, as counterinsurgents. Buster Leach was too dumb to have in-

vented that transvestite travesty, and I am smart enough not to have.

In the military grips, we were shackled spectators, forced now to watch. Lon Harlow was out of sight under the huddle waving his trousers.

But quiet was gone; everybody in the Outdoors Inn stampeded toward the dance floor—heavy ones lumbering and trumpeting, fawn-haired women leaping for front places, ox-browed burlies horning in wherever they could, and gangly specimens spindling their necks up to see over other heads, all with cacophonous bruiting, a wild scene. They stopped at the arc of brilliant lights circling the green concrete where three times nightly Llewellyn's heifers strained at their halters. Arranged to see, the crowd rumbled.

The group around Lon Harlow pushed him into the arena. (He did not have lace on the OD drawers he wore; they came, appropriately enough, from a Post Exchange.) At first, I thought he was hurt; he made about three steps limping. Then I remembered that no pain could make him limp. One of his loafers was gone, lost when his pants were. I know we can't read faces correctly for the feelings behind them; if I should say Harlow's face expressed anger or fright or sorrow, I'd be seeing there what I wanted to see. Objectively, I can say he did three things: first, he looked Fay straight in the eye; second, he sighed—I saw it but could not hear it for the barks and wheezes; third, he lifted his shod foot to the opposite hand,

removed his loafer, and tossed it toward his table. In the drab drawers, his hair seeming longer mussed, he stood still, barefoot no more than five-five.

Buster Leach was closer to us, twelve inches taller than Harlow, heavier by forty pounds at least, long arms dangling almost to his knees. The perspective exaggerated the mismatch, as I saw it from Buster's side.

Buster's move in the mad game. A lurch forward, arms outstretched to embrace Harlow and smother him. Fast. But not so fast as Harlow. The little man passed under Leach's arm and gave him an open-handed smack on the tail. Buster spun, red at the laughter, to find that Harlow and he had diametrically exchanged positions. With Harlow on our side, perspective did not improve his chances. Buster, crouched, still loomed like a magnified man.

Curiously, as if what they had just done was a rehearsal, Buster and Harlow repeated themselves, Buster grappling air, Harlow going under that terrific right arm to put another stinging spank on Buster's behind. Did Harlow hope to ridicule Buster into in-caution? I saw no hope for any tactics; the nearly naked Harlow was sure to be minced.

Buster started the step a third time. Harlow must have sensed what was coming; he did not move or duck in either direction. Buster, expecting him to, had stopped midgrab and swung both arms out low to catch him. In the moment Buster's face was thrust

AN ANGRY MILITARY MAN RENDERED IN A PERFECTLY NEUTRAL TONE

forward and his arms back, Harlow cracked a left hook off the big chin and used his weight following to land a sharp right jab on the same spot (Buster was so much taller that any blow by Harlow was an upper-cut). Buster sprawled on the concrete.

Now the cries from the crowd became intelligible: "come on, Buster"; "let im have it"; "keep yer mits up, boy"; "attababy." Familiar yells, they rose like forty-three-inch bats around the lighted circle.

Buster got up with ease. He was tough—two hard clips on the chin and the fall to the floor were nothing. He grinned, I think. If it was a grin, it was the only one I ever saw on that ugly face. He leaned toward Harlow again and ran with those crushing arms spread. With another variation on the basic routine, Harlow jumped close to the flailing knees, whisked under the right arm, struck toward the butt—but Buster had twirled. Harlow's palm slapped the trunk-like left hip, and Buster's autogyro left arm pasted a backhand on Harlow's chest. Harlow fell and immediately rolled, but Buster, anticipating, was at the right place to pin him.

Harlow's head was toward us, and we could see his too-short arms trying to pound fists on Buster's kidneys. Buster grabbed Harlow's hair, pulled, pushed, knocked the skull twice on the cement. I supposed it was all over, but on the third drive downward, Harlow tensed his neck, and Buster could not bang the small head again. His very smallness helping, Harlow lay back suddenly, slipped his knees under Buster's body, got a foot under that swelling chin, kicked. Buster flew off him, arms scalloping the air. Harlow leaped up, his back to us, the long hair above his shoulder blades bloodied by ooze from his wounded head.

Fay, who had crept between Bud and me where we were held, moaned—it must have been loud for me to hear it in the din, but I could not turn to her. Buster had risen to attack again.

Except for the gory hair and the flecks of green ground in his back, Harlow looked no worse. He was not swaying, but seemed in perfect control of himself. I thought he didn't realize his scalp was scraped—maybe his skull was broken—he could not know how damaged he was.

When Buster reached him, Harlow—caught once—had learned. He threw his body into a block across Buster's thighs, and from six feet up Buster's face crash-dived into the cement. Harlow's feet and hands stopped his own agile fall, and he stood waiting for Buster to get up.

Less easily this time, Buster climbed to a stand, his face a mess. His profile was almost a straight line; the harsh floor had flattened the frame of his nose into a bleeding pulp. He tottered; he surely knew the whole idea of him had taken a runious plunge into the concrete. He leaned toward Harlow, staggered, caught himself, turned around to the cluster of soldiers behind him, then back—and in his hand I saw a dark blade. (By Christmas, I would know its dirty redundant name—trench knife; I'd have my own.)

I tried to holler a warning; the screams of the egging crowd covered it. I jerked hard; neither arm got loose from the man holding it, and my third soldier, behind me, put a lock around my neck. Grinding my eyes as far right as I could, I saw Bud and the other musicians struggling, unable to break away. Harlow *has* handled alligators, I told myself. But a gorilla with a knife—

Buster was dangerously steadier; he shook his daze, poised, lurched. Harlow, apparently as fresh as ever, sprang to meet him, feinting right, going left, and stuck his foot where Buster's face had splattered blood on the concrete. An irregular red ink-blot, it changed shape as Harlow's foot slipped through it. Unbalanced, Harlow slid belly up into the knife. Buster turned, his broad rear putting Harlow out of our sight. When the fouled uniform moved, we saw Harlow opposite, as in the beginning, but the handle of the trench knife jutted out just beneath his ribs. Each man threw several vague shadows—the klieg lights shone at angles on the circle—and the shadows merged together.

Harlow's face stayed unchanged, but again he looked at Fay—was he reassuring her?—kept his eyes on her while he pulled the knife out and tossed it toward his table as casually as he had thrown his shoe. A thin trickle of blood leaked out from the cut. It ought to have been over, the soldiers holding us ought to have let us go, Harlow ought to have folded up, Buster ought to have understood his enemy—"ought to have" is a terrible way to say anything.

When Buster leaned forward again, he was a little unsteady, but his power remained deadly. Maybe loss of blood dulled him. He was a shade slow. Harlow coaxed the big head down, clopped three blows on its chin, and rode Buster to the dance floor. Lying on his back, Buster got around Harlow the smothering embrace that was his first object. Their heads were toward us, Harlow's cheek at Buster's neck, his small hand pushing upward on the clobbered chin.

Then Harlow's lips drew apart, and his only bigness, his teeth, glinted. Now, Lon, he is down for the count, I thought—I hoped—yes, bite the life out of that throat; be what Dartmouth says. But Harlow was a Dartmouth gentleman, only gritting his teeth with effort. My jaws ached churning out saliva.

The question was whether Buster's squeeze would cut off Harlow's air or whether Harlow's hand, a lever on Buster's chin, would stop the squeeze. Harlow couldn't but I could feel his ribs cracking. Buster—as if his neck broke—went limp, his arms falling off Harlow. At that moment everything seemed to go limp; the crowd hushed for a third silence, the soldiers holding us relaxed their grips, a draft bent the candle flames, but Harlow was standing up by Buster's supine length. For the first time, Harlow reeled a

little. He threw a foot forward to catch himself, and the foot was on Buster as Harlow straightened. Suddenly I saw the Virginia flag with its winner's foot on a loser's body. *Sic semper tyrannis*" my uncle Jeb Lee Davis translated, in his inverted way none of us in the family understood, as "Git you foot offa mah neck, you dadblame rascal."

But the scene was Tarzan's in my loose mind. Harlow's fists came together at the cut in his middle—I was sure he was going to drum on his chest, but maybe he was meeting some internal pressure with external. His head tipped back—I guess everybody in the Outdoors Inn expected the scream of a triumphant bull ape. Harlow's mouth opened—the flashing white of his teeth was there; then a fountain of blood gushed up. In the quiet we could hear it spatter on Buster, and it kept spattering.

At Ripley's Believe-It-or-Not Odditorium in Chicago a man drank about forty pitchers of water and then spewed it up to put out a fire an attendant had lit in a brazier. Please, Mr. Ripley, I'd rather Not.

Harlow's blood seemed endless—the brightest, most exciting color in nature flushed us. Even in the horror of the context, that living red was still gorgeous. Gradually the fountain sagged and Harlow sagged—he fell to make an *x* across Buster.

What I felt is confused and nameless, but it had an object: Fay. I turned toward her just as Bud did from the other side. Bud's face—his brows down dark, his nostrils wide, his snarling mouth baring clenched teeth—shook me; I did not know before that he could be fierce. My thought was—for Fay—"Oh, Lord, damn innocence"—but Bud's face stopped words. As I saw it melt, I knew he must have been shocked by my face, which I felt softening. The moment when we saw each other with changing masks was short: Fay's head was sinking. We caught her as she fainted.

Hurrying past, Jimmy Steele said, "Take care of her. I'll see about Harlow."

We carried Fay—nobody interfered—to her cabin. On the purple counterpane she was pale through her tan, embalmed. I put pillows under her legs and Bud rubbed her wrists. She stirred and hummed a moan. Without focusing, her eyes half opened. She said, "He couldn't feel it—it didn't hurt—he didn't know." And she whited out again.

Bud said, "I just hope I never feel what he felt." Thoughtless Fay; she probably would have guessed that Oedipus felt nothing after his feet healed except the prick in his eyes, that he was a hero in a simple story of Mother Goose.

I put a hot washcloth on her forehead, Bud slapped her hands, and slowly she faded in. Jimmy Steele came through the open door to say Harlow and Leach had been hauled away in a weapons carrier.

Groggy, Fay sat up. "Jimmy, he's all right, isn't he? Lon's going to be all right?"

Jimmy Steele did not hesitate. He smiled, "Oh,

yeah, Fay, I'm sure he'll be all right."

Ah, Jimmy Steele, how could *you* ever be other than sure?

The stanzas done, only the burden of Lon Harlow is left. I go slow with it, as a man should when he is developing a little coda. Having a Harlow at the top of my head sometimes makes me feel lonely, sometimes ridiculous, sometimes synthetic. Although his story, as far as I can tell it, ended with the fight, the effects did not. For instance, that night I stood Theda up, didn't look for her at all. But a couple of times earlier when the Outdoors Inn was full of khaki lust, I had heard her call one of our regular soldiers Warner Crackster. She had repeated the proper noun to let me know the jig jig was up. A minor effect; but Lon Harlow had a more important one I must mention.

After about three of Bud's best arrangements later that summer, after sweet Fay's cruel departure from us, and after all of Jimmy Steele's solos, the next big thing was Pearl Harbor. To avoid crawling with the Infantry, I volunteered for the Army Air Force. To avoid the safe and same alternation of KP and guard duty, I volunteered for aerial gunnery school. Safe may be tolerable, but hell with that same. In Europe the B-17 flew my squadron, and I was a tail gunner. Bud (he was a Navigation Officer on a troop carrier in the Pacific's worst landings and through the entire war diddled with his direction-finding equipment) said in a V-letter that mine was nice work and that I doubtless loved the title. He even said I had a complex. Maybe, but *he* wrote the story about the sheep castrater. I've read his MS., and in it he related those horrible teeth (Sears still sells them) to Sigmund Freud's prosthesis. After knowing him longer than

thirty years, I can't say yet whether Bud's stubborn streak exceeds his cunning.

And I can't say what the war was all about, because Lon Harlow confused me. Everybody around me seemed sure enough, but I couldn't be. To say how Lon Harlow shaped the way I saw the war would take a writer rather than a piano player in a home for retired vaudevillians. They sleep all day and at night perform for one another acts from their youth. At rehearsals they work primarily on timing, and my main instruction is "Vamp till ready." It's a bore, but it's my food and drink.

Throughout the war, Harlow was always up there in my skull. People who were supposed to shoot at me did. I shot at people I was supposed to, all the time knowing nothing of what it might mean. If I had sense enough to understand Lon Harlow, his fight, the paradigm, I could come closer to understanding the war, the big fight, the people who made it. It's up to me; nobody else can interpret it all for me, and I may never. Figuring out Lon Harlow or the war is as tough as putting what jazz is in words, and it's dangerous, like trying from about forty yards away to read the expression on an albino face, to decide whether that glint from the mouth is a smile or a baring of fangs. Maybe, with all its earthy space, America is the ideal place to work it through, once I absorb the red grief slanting its gaze on my memory's back door.

I was not the only one to escape and wish he could tell it. We many rememberers join one another often in audiences applauding less spectacular shows. Some *fake* freaks, a poor sign. A good sign is that I forget the names of bad clarinet players. I wish I couldn't remember Guy Lombardo, but everybody knows who he is.

Illustrated by George Bireline

THE UGLIEST PILGRIM

By Doris Betts

I sit in the bus station, nipping chocolate peel off a Mounds candy bar with my teeth, then pasting the cocoanut filling to the roof of my mouth. The lump will dissolve there, slowly, and seep into me the way dew seeps into flowers.

I like to separate flavors that way. Always I lick the salt off cracker tops before taking my first bite.

Somebody sees me with my suitcase, paper sack, and a ticket in my lap. "You going someplace, Violet?"

Stupid. People in Spruce Pine are dumb and, since I look dumb, say dumb things to me. I turn up my face as if to count those dead flies piled under the light bulb. He walks away—a fat man, could be anybody. I stick out my tongue at his back; the candy oozes down. If I could stop swallowing, it would drip into my lung and I could breathe vanilla.

Whoever it was, he won't glance back. People in Spruce Pine don't like to look at me, full face.

A Greyhound bus pulls in, blows air; the driver stands by the door. He's black-headed, maybe part Cherokee, with heavy shoulders but a weak chest. He thinks well of himself—I can tell that. I open my notebook and copy his name off the metal plate so I can call him by it when he drives me home again. And next week, won't Mr. Wallace Weatherman be surprised to see how well I'm looking!

I choose the front seat behind Mr. Weatherman, settle my bag with the hat in it, then open the lined composition book again. Maybe it's half-full of writing. Even the empty pages toward the back have one repeated entry, high, printed off Mama's torn catechism: GLORIFY GOD AND ENJOY HIM FOREVER.

I finish Mr. Weatherman off in my book while he's running his motor and getting us onto the highway. His nose is too broad, his dark eyes too skimpy—nothing in his face I want—but the hair is nice. I write that down, "Black hair?" I'd want it to curl, though, and be soft as a baby's.

Two others are on the bus, a nigger soldier and an old woman whose jaw sticks out like a shelf. There grow, on the backs of her hands, more veins than skin. One fat blue vessel, curling from wrist to knuckle, would be good; so on one page I draw a sample hand and let blood wind across it like a river. I write at the bottom: "Praise God, it is started. May 29, 1969," and turn to a new sheet. The paper's lumpy and I flip back to the thick envelope stuck there with adhesive tape. I can't lose that.

We're driving, now, at the best speed Mr. Weatherman can make on these winding roads. On my side there is nothing out the bus window but granite rock, jagged and wet in patches. The old lady and the nigger can see red rhododendron on the slope of Roan Mountain. I'd like to own a tight dress that flower color, and breasts to go under it. I write in my notebook, very small, the word "breasts," and turn quickly to another page. AND ENJOY HIM FOREVER.

The soldier bends as if to tie his shoes, but instead zips open a canvas bag and sticks both hands inside. When finally he sits back, one hand is clenched around something hard. He catches me watching. He yawns and scratches his ribs, but the right fist sets very lightly on his knee, and when I turn he drinks something out of its cup and throws his head quickly back like a bird or a chicken. You'd think I could smell it, big as my nose is.

Across the aisle the old lady says, "You going far?" She shows me a set of tan, artificial teeth.

"Oklahoma."

"I never been there. I hear the trees give out." She pauses so I can ask politely where she's headed. "I'm going to Nashville," she finally says. "The country music capital of the world. My son lives there and works in the cellophane plant."

I draw in my notebook a box and two arrows. I criss-cross the box.

"He's got three children not old enough to be in school yet."

I sit very still, adding new boxes, drawing baseballs

RED CLAY READER 33

in some, looking busy for fear she might bring out their pictures from her big straw pocketbook. The funny thing is, she's looking past my head though there's nothing out that window but rock wall sliding by. I mumble, "It's hot in here."

Angrily she says, "I had eight children myself."

My pencil flies to get the boxes stacked, eight-deep, in a pyramid. "Hope you have a nice visit."

"It's not a visit. I maybe will move." She is hypnotized by the stone and the furry moss in its cracks. Her eyes used to be green. Maybe, when young, she was red-haired and Irish. If she'll stop talking, I want to think about trying green eyes with that Cherokee hair. Her lids droop; she looks drowsy. "I am right tired of children," she says and lays her head back on the white rag they button on these seats.

Now that her eyes are covered, I can study that face—china-white, and worn thin as tissue so light comes between her bones and shines through her whole head. I picture the light going around and around her skull, like water spinning in a jar. If I could wait to be eighty, even my face might grind down and look softer. But I'm ready, in case the Preacher mentions that. Did Elisha make Naaman bear into old age his leprosy? Didn't Jesus heal the withered hand, even on Sunday, without waiting for the work week to start? And put back the ear of Malchus with a touch? As soon as Job had learned enough, did his boils fall away?

Lord, I have learned enough.

The old lady sleeps while we roll downhill and up again, then turn so my side of the bus looks over the valley and its thickety woods where, as a girl, I pulled armloads of galax, fern, laurel, and hemlock to have some spending money. I spent it for magazines full of women with permanent waves. Behind us, the nigger shuffles a deck of cards and deals to himself by fives. Draw poker—I could beat him. My Papa showed me, long winter days and nights snowed-in on the mountain. He said Poker would teach me arithmetic. It taught me there are four ways to make a royal flush and, with two players, it's an even chance one of them holds a pair on the deal. And when you try to draw from a pair to four-of-a-kind, discard the kicker; it helps your odds.

The soldier deals smoothly, using his left hand only with his thumb on top. Papa was good at that. He looks up and sees my whole face with its scar, but he keeps his eyes level as if he has seen worse things; and his left hand drops cards evenly and in rhythm. Like a turtle, laying eggs.

I close my eyes and the riffle of his deck rests me to the next main stop where I write in my notebook: "Praise God for Johnson City, Tennessee, and all the state to come. I am on my way."

At Kingsport, Mr. Weatherman calls rest stop and I go straight through the terminal to the ladies' toilet and look hard at my face in the mirror. I must remem-

ber to start the Preacher on the scar first of all—the only thing about me that's even on both sides.

Lord! I am so ugly!

Maybe the Preacher will claim he can't heal ugliness. And I'm going to spread my palms by my ears and show him—This is a crippled face! An infirmity! Would he do for a kidney or liver what he withholds from a face? The Preacher once stuttered, I read someplace, and God bothered with that. Why not me? When the Preacher labors to heal the sick in his Tulsa auditorium, he asks us at home to lay our fingers on the television screen and pray for God's healing. He puts forth his own ten fingers and we match them, pad to pad, on that glass. I have tried that, Lord, and the Power was too filtered and thinned down for me.

I touch my hand now to this cold mirror glass, and cover all but my pimpled chin, or wide nose, or a single red-brown eye. And nothing's too bad by itself. But when they're put together?

I've seen the Preacher wrap his hot, blessed hands on a club foot and cry out HEAL in his funny way that sounds like the word *Hell* broken into two pieces. Will he not cry out, too, when he sees this poor, clubbed face? I will be to him as Goliath was to David, a need so giant it will drive God to action.

I comb out my pine needle hair. I think I would like blonde curls and Irish eyes, and I want my mouth so large it will never be done with kissing.

The old lady comes in the toilet and catches me pinching my bent face. She jerks back once, looks sad, then pets me with her twiggy hand. "Listen, honey," she says, "I had looks once. It don't amount to much."

I push right past. Good people have nearly turned me against you, Lord. They open their mouths for the milk of human kindness and boiling oil spews out.

So I'm half running through the terminal and into the cafe, and I take the first stool and call down the counter, "Tuna fish sandwich," quick. Living in the mountains, I eat fish every chance I get and wonder what the sea is like. Then I see I've sat down by the nigger soldier. I do not want to meet his gaze, since he's a wonder to me, too. We don't have many black men in the mountains. Mostly they live east in Carolina, on the flat land, and pick cotton and tobacco instead of apples. They seem to me like foreigners. He's absently shuffling cards the way some men twiddle thumbs. On the stool beyond him is a paratrooper, white, and they're talking about what a bitch the army is. Being sent to the same camp has made them friends already.

I roll a dill pickle slice through my mouth—a wheel, a bitter wheel. Then I start on the sandwich and it's chicken by mistake when I've got chickens all over my back yard.

"Don't bother with the beer," says the black one. "I've got better on the bus." They come to some agreement and deal out cards on the counter.

It's just too much for me. I lean over behind the nigger's back and say to the paratrooper, "I wouldn't play with him." Neither one moves. "He's a mechanic." They look at each other, not at me. "It's a way to cheat on the deal."

The paratrooper sways backward on his stool and stares around out of eyes so blue that I want them, right away, and maybe his pale blonde hair. I swallow a crusty, half-chewed bite. "One-handed grip; the mechanic's grip. It's the middle finger. He can second deal and bottom deal. He can buckle the top card with his thumb and peep."

"I be damn," says the paratrooper.

The nigger spins around and bares his teeth at me, but it's half a grin. "Lady, you want to play?"

I slide my dishes back. "I get mad if I'm cheated."

"And mean when you're mad." He laughs a laugh so deep it makes me re-taste that bittersweet chocolate off the candy bar. He offers the deck to cut, so I pull out the center and restack it three ways. A little air blows through his upper teeth. "I'm Grady Fliggins and they call me Flick."

The paratrooper reaches a hand down the counter to shake mine. "Monty Harrill. From near to Raleigh."

"And I'm Violet Karl. Spruce Pine. I'd rather play five card stud."

By the time the bus rolls on, we've moved to its wider back seat playing serious cards with a fifty cent ante. My money's sparse, but I'm good and the deck is clean. The old lady settles into my front seat, stiffer than plaster. Sometimes she throws back a hurt look.

Monty, the paratrooper, plays soft. But Flick's so good he doesn't even need to cheat, though I watch him close. He drops out quick when his cards are bad; he makes me bid high to see what he's got; and the few times he bluffs, I'm fooled. He's no talker. Monty, on the other hand, says often, "Whose play is it?"'till I know that's his clue phrase for a pair. He lifts his cards close to his nose and gets quiet when planning to bluff. And he'd rather use wild cards but we won't. Ah, but he's pretty, though!

After we've swapped a little money, mostly the para-trooper's, Flick pours us a drink in some cups he stole in Kingsport and asks, "Where'd you learn to play?"

I tell him about growing up on a mountain, high, with Mama dead; and shuffling cards by a kerosene lamp with my Papa. When I passed fifteen, we'd drink together, too. Applejack or a beer he made from potato peel.

"And where you headed now?" Monty's wind-burned in a funny pattern, with pale goggle circles that start high on his cheeks. Maybe it's something paratroopers wear.

"It's a pilgrimage." They lean back with their drinks. "I'm going to see this preacher in Tulsa, the one that heals, and I'm coming home pretty. Isn't that healing?" Their still faces make me nervous. "I'll even trade if he says . . . I'll take somebody else's weak eyes or deaf ears. I could stand limping a little."

The nigger shakes his black head, snickering.

"I tried to get to Charlotte when he was down there

with his eight-pole canvas cathedral tent that seats nearly fifteen thousand people, but I didn't have money then. Now what's so funny?" I think for a minute I am going to have to take out my notebook, and unglue the envelope and read them all the scripture I have looked up on why I should be healed. Monty looks sad for me, though, and that's worse. "Let the Lord twist loose my foot or give me a cough, so long as I'm healed of my looks while I'm still young enough. . ." I stop and tip up my plastic cup. Young enough for you, blue-eyed boy, and your brothers.

"Listen," says Flick in a high voice, "Let me go with you and be there for that swapping." He winks one speckled eye.

"I'll not take black skin, no offense." He's offended, though, and lurches across the moving bus and falls into a far seat. "Well, you as much as said you'd swap it off!" I call. "What's wrong if I don't want it any more than you?"

Monty slides closer. "You're not much to look at," he grants, sweeping me up and down till I nearly glow blue from his eyes. Shaking his head. "And what now? Thirty?"

"Twenty-eight. His drink and his cards, and I hurt Flick's feelings. I didn't mean that." I'm scared, too. Maybe, unlike Job, I haven't learned enough. Who ought to be expert in hurt feelings? Me, that's who.

"And you live by yourself?"

I start to say No, there's men falling all over each other going in and out my door. He sees my face, don't he? It makes me call, "Flick? I'm sorry." Not one movement. "Yes. By myself." Five years now, since Papa had heart failure and fell off the high back porch and rolled downhill in the gravel till the hobble bushes stopped him. I found him past sunset, cut from the rocks but not much blood showing. And what there was, dark, and already jellied.

Monty looks at me carefully before making up his mind to say, "That preacher's a fake. You ever see a doctor agree to what he's done?"

"Might be." I'm smiling. I tongue out the last liquor in my cup. I've thought of all that, but it may be what I believe is stronger than him faking. That he'll be electrified by my trust, the way a magnet can get charged against its will. He might be a lunatic or a dope fiend, and it still not matter.

Monty says, "Flick, you plan to give us another drink?"

"No." He acts like he's going to sleep.

"I just wouldn't count on that preacher too much." Monty cleans his nails with a matchbook corner and sometimes gives me an uneasy look. "Things are mean and ugly in this world, I mean *act* ugly, do ugly, be ugly."

He's wrong. When I leave my house, I can walk for miles and everything's beautiful. Even the rattlesnakes have grace. I don't mind his worried looks, since I'm writing in my notebook how we met and my win-nings—a good sign, to earn money on a trip. I like the way army barbers trim his hair. I wish I could touch it.

"Took one furlough in your mountains. Pretty country. Maybe hard to live in? Makes you feel little." He looks toward Flick and says softer, "Makes you feel like the night sky does. So many stars."

"Some of them big as daisies." It's easy to live in, though. Some mornings a deer and I scare up each other in the brush, and his heart stops, and mine stops. Everything stops till he plunges away. The next pulse beat nearly knocks you down. "Monty, doesn't your hair get lighter in the summers? That might be a good color hair to ask for in Tulsa. Then I could turn colors like the leaves. Spell your last name for me."

He does, and says I sure am funny. Then he spells Grady Fliggins and I write that, too. He's curious about my book so I flip through and offer to read him parts. Even with his eyes shut, Flick is listening. I read them about my Papa's face, a chunky block face, not much different from the Preacher's square one. After Papa died I wrote that to slow down how fast I was forgetting him. I tell Monty parts of my lists: that you can get yellow dye out of gopherwood and Noah built his ark from that, and maybe it stained the water. That a cow eating snakeroot might give poison milk. I pass him a pressed maypop flower I'm carrying to Tulsa, because the crown of thorns and the crucifixion nails grow in its center, and each piece of the bloom stands for one of the Apostles.

"It's a mollypop vine," says Flick out of one corner of his mouth. "And it makes a green ball that pops when you step on it." He stretches. "Deal you some blackjack?"

For no reason, Monty says, "We oughtn't to let her go."

We play blackjack till supper stop and I write in my book, "Praise God for Knoxville and two new friends." I've not had many friends. At school in the valley, I sat in the back rows, reading, a hand spread on my face. I was smart, too; but if you let that show, you had to stand for the class and present different things.

When the driver cuts out the lights, the soldiers give me a whole seat, and a dufflebag for a pillow. I hear them whispering, first about women, then about me; but after awhile I don't hear that anymore.

By the time we hit Nashville, the old lady makes the bus wait while she begs me to stop with her. "Harvey won't mind. He's a good boy." She will not even look at Monty and Flick. "You can wash and change clothes and catch a new bus tomorrow."

"I'm in a hurry. Thank you." I have picked a lot of galax to pay for this trip.

"A girl alone. A girl that maybe feels she's got to prove something?" The skin on her neck shivers. "Some people might take advantage."

Maybe when I ride home under my new face, that will be some risk. I shake my head, and as she gets off she whispers something to Mr. Weatherman about

looking after me. It's wasted, though, because a new driver takes his place and he looks nearly as bad as I do—oily faced and toad-shaped, with eyeballs a dingy color and streaked with blood. He's the flatlands driver, I guess, because he leans back and drops one warty hand on the wheel and we go so fast and steady you can hardly tell it.

Since Flick is the tops in cards and we're tired of that, it's Monty's turn to brag on his motorcycle. He talks all across Tennessee till I think I could ride one by hearsay alone, that my wrist knows by itself how far to roll the throttle in. It's a Norton and he rides it in Scrambles and Enduro events, in his leathers, with spare parts and tools glued all over him with black electrician's tape.

"So this bastard tells me, 'Zip up your jacket because when I run over you I want some traction.'"

Flick is playing solitaire. "You couldn't get me on one of them killing things."

"One day I'm coming through Spruce Pine, flat out, throw Violet up behind me! We're going to lean all the way through them mountains. Sliding the right foot and then sliding the left." Monty lays his head back on the seat beside me, rolls it, watches. "How you like that? Take you through creeks and ditches like you was on a skate board. You can just holler and hang on."

Lots of women have, I bet.

"The Norton's got the best front forks of anybody. It'll nearly roll up a tree trunk and ride down the other side." He demonstrates on the seat back. I keep writing. These are new things, two stroke and four stroke, picking your line on a curve, Milwaukee iron. It will all come back to me in the winters, when I reread these pages.

Flick says he rode on a Harley once. "Turned over and got drug. No more."

They argue about what he should have done instead of turning over. Finally Monty drifts off to sleep, his head leaning at me, slowly, so I look down on his crisp, light hair. I pat it as easy as a cat would, and it tickles my palm. I'd almost ask them in Tulsa to make me a man if I could have hair like his, and a beard, and feel so different in so many places.

He slides closer in his sleep. One eyebrow wrinkles against my shoulder. Looking our way, Flick smokes a cigarette, then reads some magazine he keeps rolled in his belt. Monty makes a deep noise against my arm as if, while he slept, his throat had cleared itself. I shift and his whole head is on my shoulder now. Its weight makes me breathe shallow.

I rest my eyes. If I should turn, his hair would barely touch my cheek, the scarred one, like a shoebrush. I do turn and it does. For miles he sleeps that way and I almost sleep. Once when we take a long curve he rolls against me, and one of his hands drifts up and then drops in my lap. Just there, where the creases are.

I would not want God's Power to turn me, after all, into a man. His breath is so warm. Everywhere, my skin is singing. Praise God for that.

When I get my first look at the Mississippi River, the pencil goes straight into my pocketbook. How much praise would that take?

"Is the sea like this?"

"Not except they're both water," Flick says. He's not mad anymore. "Tell you what, Vi-oh-LETTE. When Monty picks you up on his cycle," (Sickle, he calls it) "you ride down to the beaches—Cherry Grove, O.D., around there. Where they work the big nets in the fall and drag them up on the sand with trucks at each end, and men to their necks in the surf."

"You do that?"

"I know people that do. And afterward they strip and dress by this big fire on the beach."

And they make chowder while this cold wind is blowing! I know that much, without asking. In a big black pot that sits on that whipping fire. I think they might let me sit with them and stir the pot. It's funny how much, right now, I feel like praising all the good things I've never seen, in places I haven't been.

Everybody had to get off the bus and change in Memphis, and most of them wait a long time. I've taken the long way, coming here; but some of Mama's cousins live in Memphis and might rest me overnight. Monty says they plan to stay the night, too, and break the long trip.

"They know you're coming, Violet?" It's Flick says my name that way, in pieces, carefully: Vi-oh-LETTE. Monty is lazier: Viiiiiii-Lut. They make me feel like more than one.

"I've never even met these cousins. But soon as I call up and tell them who I am and that I'm here . . ."

"We'll stay some hotel tonight and then ride on. Why don't you come with us?" Monty is carrying my scuffed bag. Flick swings the paper sack. "You know us better than them."

"Kin people," grunts Flick, "can be a bad surprise."

Monty is nodding his head. "Only cousin I had got drunk and drove this tractor over his baby brother. Did it on purpose, too." I see by his face that Monty has made this up, for my sake.

"Your cousins might not even live here anymore. I bet it's been years since you heard from a one."

"We're picking a cheap hotel, in case that's a worry."

I never thought they might have moved. "How cheap?"

When Flick says "Under five," I nod; and my things go right up on their shoulders as I follow them into a Memphis cab. The driver takes for granted I'm Monty's afflicted sister and names a hotel right off. He treats me with pity and good manners.

And the hotel he chooses is cheap, all right, where ratty salesmen with bad territories spend half the night drinking in their rooms. Plastic palm bushes and a worn rug the color of wet cigars. I get Room 210

and they're down the hall in the teens. They stand in my doorway and watch me drop both shoes and walk the bed in bare feet. When Monty opens my window, we can hear some kitchen underneath—a fan, clattering noise, a man's crackly voice singing about the California earthquake.

It scares me, suddenly, to know I can't remember how home sounds. Not one bird call, nor the water over rocks. There's so much you can't save by writing down.

"Smell that grease," says Flick, and shakes his head till his lips flutter. "I'm finding an ice machine. You, Vi-oh-LETTE, come on down in awhile."

Monty's got a grin I'll remember if I never write a word. He waves. "Flick and me going to get drunker than my old cousin and put wild things in your book. Going to draw dirty pictures. You come on down and get drunk enough to laugh."

But after a shower, damp in my clean slip, even this bed like a roll of fence wire feels good, and I fall asleep wondering if that rushing noise is a river wind, and how long I can keep it in my mind.

Monty and Flick edge into my dream. Just their voices, first, from way downhill. Somewhere in a Shonny Haw thicket. "Just different," Monty is saying. "That's all. Different. Don't make some big thing out of it." He doesn't sound happy. "Nobody else," he says.

Is that Flick singing? No, because the song goes on while his voice says, "Just so . . ." and then some words I don't catch. "It don't hurt?" Or maybe, "You don't hurt?" I hear them climbing my tangled hill, breaking sticks and knocking the little stones loose. I'm trying to call to them which way the path is, but I can't make noise because the Preacher took my voice and put it in a black bag and carried it to a sick little boy in Iowa.

They find the path, anyway. And now they can see my house and me standing little by the steps. I know how it looks from where they are: the wood rained on till the siding's almost silver; and behind the house a wet-weather waterfall that's cut a stream bed downhill and grown pin cherry and bee balm on both sides. The high rock walls by the waterfall are mossy and slick, but I've scraped one place and hammered a mean-looking gray head that leans out of the hillside and stares down the path at whoever comes. I've been here so long by myself that I talk to it, sometimes. Right now I'd say, "Look yonder, We've got company at last!" if my voice wasn't gone.

"You can't go by looks," Flick is saying as they climb. He ought to know. Ahead of them, warblers separate and fly out on two sides. Everything moves out of their path if I could just see it—tree frogs and mosquitoes. Maybe the worms drop deeper just before a footstep falls.

"Without the clothes, it's not a hell of a lot improved," says Monty, and I know suddenly they are inside the house with me, inside my very room, and my room today's in Memphis. "There's one thing, though," Monty says, standing over my bed. "Good looks in a woman is almost like a wall. She can use it to shut you outside. You never know what she's like, that's all." He's wearing a T-shirt and his dog tags jingle. "Most of the time I don't even miss knowing that."

And Flick says, disgusted, "I knew that much in grammar school. You sure are slow. It's not the face you screw." If I opened my eyes, I could see him now, behind Monty. He says, "After awhile, you don't even notice faces. I always thought, in a crowd, my Mother might not pick Daddy out."

"*My* mother could," says Monty. "He was always the one *started* the fight."

I stretch and open my eyes. It's a plain slip, cotton, that I sewed myself and makes me look too white and skinny as a sapling.

"She's waking up."

When I point, Monty hands me the blouse off the doorknob. Flick says they've carried me a soda-pop plus something to spruce it up. They sit stiffly on two hard chairs till I've buttoned on my skirt. I sip the drink, cold but peppery, and prop on the bed with the pillows. "I dreamed you both came where my house is, on the mountain, and it had rained so the waterfall was working. I felt real proud of that."

After two drinks we go down to the noisy restaurant with that smelly grease. And after that, to a picture show. Monty grins widely when the star comes on the screen. The spit on his teeth shines, even in the dark. Seeing what kind of woman he really likes, black-haired as a gypsy and with a juicy mouth, I change all my plans. My eyes, too, must turn up on the ends and when I bend down my breasts must fall forward and push at each other. When the star does that in the picture, the cowboy rubs his mustache low in the front of her neck.

In the darkness, Monty takes my hand and holds it in his swelling lap. To me it seems funny that my hand, brown and crusty from hoeing and chopping, is harder than his. I guess you don't get calluses, rolling a motorcycle throttle. He rubs his thumb up and down my middle finger. Oh, I would like to ride fast behind him, spraddle-legged, with my arms wrapped on his belt and I would lay my face between his sharp shoulderblades.

That night when I've slept awhile, I hear something brushing the rug in the hall. I slip to my door. It's very dark. I press myself, face first, to the wood. There's breathing on the other side. I feel I get fatter, standing there, that even my own small breasts might now be made to touch. I round both shoulders to see. The movement jars the door and it trembles slightly in its frame.

From the far side, by the hinges, somebody whispers, "Vi-oh-LETTE?"

Now I stand very still. The wood feels cooler on my skin, or else I have grown very warm. Oh, I could love anybody! There is so much of me now, they could line up strangers in the hall and let me hold each one better than he had ever been held before!

Slowly I turn the knob, but Flick's breathing is gone. The corridor's empty. I leave the latch off.

Late in the night when the noise from the kitchen is over, he comes into my room. I wake when he bumps on a chair, swears, then scrabbles at the footboard.

"Viiiiii-lut?"

I slide up in bed. I'm not ready, not now, but he's here. I spread both arms wide. In the dark he can't tell.

He feels his way onto the bed and he touches my knee and it changes. Stops being just my old knee, under his fingers. I feel the joint heat up and bubble. I push the sheet down.

He comes onto me, whispering something. I reach up to claim him.

One time he stops. He's surprised, I guess, finding he isn't the first. How can I tell him how bad that was? How long ago? The night when the 12th grade was over and one of them climbed with me all the way home? And he asked. And I thought, *I'm entitled.* Won him a five dollar bet. Didn't do nothing for me.

But this time I sing out and Monty says, "Shhhh," in my ear. And he starts over, slow, and makes me whimper one other time. Then he turns sideways to sleep and I try my face there, laid in the nest on his damp back. I reach out my tongue. He is salty and good.

Now there are two things too big for my notebook but Praise God! And for the Mississippi, too!

There is no good reason for me to ride with them all the way to Fort Smith, but since Tulsa is not expecting me, we change my ticket. Monty pays the extra. We ride through the fertile plains. The last of May becomes June and the Arkansas sun is blazing. I am stunned by this heat. At home, night means blankets and even on hot afternoons it may rain and start the waterfall. I lie against my seat for miles without a word.

"What's wrong?" Monty keeps asking; but, under the heat, I am happy. Sleepy with happiness, a lizard on a rock. At every stop Monty's off the bus, bringing me more than I can eat or drink, buying me magazines and gum. I tell him and Flick to play two-handed cards, but mostly Flick lectures him in a low voice about something.

I try to stop thinking of Memphis and think back to Tulsa. I went to the Spruce Pine library to look Tulsa up in their encyclopedia. I thought sure it would tell about the Preacher, and on what street he'd built his Hope And Glory Building for his soul crusades. Tulsa was listed in the Americana, Volume 27, Trance to Venial Sin. I got so tickled with that I forgot to write down the rest.

Now, in the hot sun, clogged up with trances and venial sins, I dream under the drone of their voices.

For some reason I remember that old lady back in Nashville, moved in with Harvey and his wife and their three children. I hope she's happy. I picture her on Harvey's back porch, baked in the sun like me, in a rocker. Snapping beans.

I've left my pencil in the hotel and must borrow one from Flick to write in my book. I put in, slowly, "This is the day which the Lord hath made." But, before Monty, what kind of days was he sending me? I cross out the line. I have this wish to praise, instead of Him, the littlest things. Honeybees, and the wet slugs under their rocks. A gnat in some farmer's eye.

I give up and hand Flick his pencil. He slides toward the aisle and whispers, "You wish you'd stayed in your mountains?"

I shake my head and a piece of my no-color hair falls into the sunlight. Maybe it even shines.

He spits on the pencil point and prints something inside a gum wrapper. "Here's my address. You keep it. Never can tell."

So I tear the paper in half and give him back mine. He reads it a long time before tucking it away, but he won't send a letter till I do—I can tell that. Through all this, Monty stares out the window. Arkansas rolls out ahead of us like a rug.

Monty has not asked for my address, nor how far uphill I live from Spruce Pine, though he could ride his motorcycle up to me, strong as its engine is. For a long time he has been sitting quietly, lighting one cigarette off another. This winter, I've got to learn smoking. How to lift my hand up so every eye will follow it to my smooth cheek.

I put Flick's paper in my pocketbook and there, inside, on a round mirror, my face is waiting in ambush for me. I see the curved scar, neat as ever, swoop from the edge of one nostril in rainbow shape across my cheek, then down toward the ear. For the first time in years, pain boils across my face as it did that day. I close my eyes under that red drowning, and see again Papa's ax head rise off its locust handle and come floating through the air, sideways, like a gliding crow. And it drops down into my face almost daintily, the edge turned just enough to slash loose a flap of skin the way you might slice straight down on the curve of a melon. My Papa is yelling, but I am under a red rain and it bears me down. I am lifted and run with through the woodyard and into the barn. Now I am slumped on his chest and the whipped horse is throwing us down the mountainside, and my head is wrapped in something big as a wet quilt. The doctor groans when he winds it off and I faint while he lifts up my flesh like the flap of a pulpy envelope, and sews the white bone out of sight.

Dizzy from the movement of the bus, I snap shut my pocketbook.

Whenever I cry, the first drop quivers there, in the curving scar, and then runs crooked on that track to the ear. I cry straight-down on the other side.

I am glad this bus has a toilet. I go there to cool my eyes with wet paper, and spit up Monty's chocolate and cola.

When I come out he's standing at the door with his fist up. "You all right, Viiii-lut? You worried or something?"

I see he pities me. In my seat again, I plan the speech I will make at Fort Smith and the laugh I will give. "Honey you're good," I'll say, laughing, "but the others were better." That ought to do it. I am quieter now than Monty is, practicing it in my mind.

It's dark when we hit Fort Smith. Everybody's face looks shadowed and different. Mine better. Monty's strange. We're saying goodbyes very fast. I start my speech twice and he misses it twice.

Then he bends over me and offers his own practiced line that I see he's worked up all across Arkansas, "I plan to be right here, Violet, in this bus station. On Monday. All day. You get off your bus when it comes through. Hear me, Viiii-lut? I'll watch for you?"

No. He won't watch. Nor I come. "My schedule won't take me this road, going back. Bye, Flick. Lots of good luck to you both."

"Promise me. Like I'm promising."

"Good luck to you, Vi-oh-LETTE." Flick lets his hand fall on my head and it feels as good as anybody's hand.

Monty shoves money at me and I shove it back. "Promise," he says, his voice furious. He tries to kiss me in the hair and I jerk so hard my nose cracks his chin. We stare, blurry-eyed and hurting. He follows Flick down the aisle, calls back, "I'm coming here Monday. See you then, hear? And you get off this bus!"

"No! I won't!"

He yells it twice more. People are staring. He's out of the bus pounding on the steel wall by my seat. I'm not going to look. The seats fill up with strangers and we ride away, nobody talking to anyone else. My nose where I hit it is going to swell—the Preacher will have to throw that in for free. I look back, but he's gone.

The lights in the bus go out again. Outside they bloom thick by the streets, then thinner, then mostly gone as we pass into the countryside. Even in the dark, I can see Oklahoma's mountains are uglier than mine. Knobs and hills, mostly. The bus drives into rain which covers up everything. At home I like that washing sound. We go deeper into the downpour. Perhaps we are under the Arkansas River after all. It seems I can feel its great weight move over me.

Before daylight, the rain tapers off and here the ground looks dry, even barren. Cattle graze across long fields. In the wind, wheatfields shiver. I can't eat anything all the way to Tulsa. It makes me homesick to see the land grow brighter and flatter and balder. That old lady was right—the trees do give out—and oil towers grow in their place. The glare's in my eyes. I write in my notebook, "Praise God for Tulsa; I am nearly there," but it takes a long time to get the words down.

One day my Papa told me how time got slow for

him when Mama died. How one week he waded through the creek and it was water, and the next week, cold molasses. How he'd lay awake a year between sundown and sunup, and in the morning I'd be a day older and he'd be three hundred and sixty-five.

It works the other way, too. In no time at all, we're into Tulsa without me knowing what we've passed. So many tall buildings. Everybody's running. They rush into taxis before I can get one to wait for me long enough to ask the driver questions. But still I'm speeded to a hotel, and the elevator yanks me to a room quicker than Elijah rode to Heaven. The room's not bad. A Gideon Bible. Inside are lots of dirty words somebody wrote. He must have been feeling bad.

I bathe and dress, trembling from my own speed, and pin on the hat which has traveled all the way from Spruce Pine for this. I feel tired. I go out into the loud streets full of fast cars. Hot metal everywhere. A taxi roars me across town to the Preacher's church.

It looks like a big insurance office, though I can tell where the chapel is by colored glass in the pointed windows. Carved in an arch over the door are the words HOPE OF GLORY BUILDING. Right away, something in me sinks. All this time I've been hearing it on t.v. as the Hope *and* Glory Building. You wouldn't think one word could make that much difference.

Inside the door, there's a list of offices and room numbers. I don't see the Preacher's name. Clerks send me down long, tiled halls, past empty air-conditioned offices. One tells me to go up two flights and ask the fat woman, and the fat woman sends me down again. I'm carrying my notebook in a dry hand, feeling as brittle as the maypop flower.

At last I wait an hour to see some assistant; very close to the Preacher, I'm told. His waiting room is chilly, the leatherette chairs worn down to the mesh. I try to remember how much TB and cancer have passed through this very room and been jerked out of people the way Jesus tore out a demon and flung him into a herd of swine. I wonder what he felt like to the swine.

After a long time, the young man calls me into his plain office—wood desk, wood chairs. Shelves of booklets and colored folders. On one wall, a colored picture of Jesus with that fairy ring of light around his head. Across from that, one of His praying hands—rougher than Monty's, smoother than mine.

The young man wears glasses with no rims. In this glare, I am reflected on each lens, Vi-oh-LETTE and Viii-lut. On his desk is a box of postcards of the Hope and Glory Building. *Of* Glory. *Of* Glory.

I am afraid.

I feel behind me for the chair.

The man explains that he is presently in charge. The Preacher's speaking in Tallahassee, his show taped weeks ahead. I never thought of it as a show before. He waits.

I reach inside my notebook where, taped shut, is the thick envelope with everything written down. I knew I could never explain things right. When have I ever been able to tell what I really felt? But it's all in there—my name, my need. The words from the Bible which must argue for me. I did not sit there nights since Papa died, counting my money and studying God's book—for nothing. Playing solitaire, then going back to search the next page and the next. Stepping outside to rest my eyes on His limitless sky, then back to the Book and the paper, building my case.

He starts to read, turns up his glitter-glass to me once to check how I look, then reads again. His chair must be hard, for he squirms in it, crosses his legs. When he has read every page, he lays the stack down, slowly takes off his glasses, folds them shining into a case. He leaves it open on his desk. Mica shines like that, in the rocks.

Then he looks at me, fully. Oh. He is plain. Almost homely. I nearly expected it. Maybe Samuel was born ugly, so who else would take him but God?

"My child," the man begins, though I'm older than he is. "I understand how you feel. And we will most certainly pray for your spirit. . ."

I shut my eyes against those two flashing faces on his spectacles. "Never mind my spirit." I see he doesn't really understand. I see he will live a long life, and not marry.

"Our Heavenly Father has purpose in all things."

Stubbornly, "Ask Him to set it aside."

"We must all trust His will."

After all these years, isn't it God's turn to trust mine? Could he not risk a little beauty on me? Just when I'm ready to ask, the sober assistant recites, "'Favor is deceitful and beauty is vain.' That's in Proverbs."

And I cry, "The crooked shall be made straight! Isaiah said that!" He draws back, as if I had brought the Gideon Bible and struck him with its most disfigured pages. "Jesus healed an impediment in speech. See my impediment! Mud on a blind man's eyes was all He needed! Don't you remember?" But he's read all that. Everything I know on my side lies, written out, under his sweaty hand. Lord, don't let me whine. But I whine, "He healed the ten lepers and only one thanked. Well, I'll thank. I promise. All my life."

He clears his long knotty throat and drones like a bee, "By the sadness of the countenance the heart is made better. Ecclesiastes. Seven. Three."

Oh, that's not fair! I skipped those parts, looking for verses that suited me! And it's wrong, besides.

I get up to leave and he asks will I kneel with him? "Let us pray together for that inner beauty."

No, I will not. I go down that hollow hall and past the echoing rooms. Without his help I find the great auditorium, lit through colored glass, with its cross of white plastic and a pinker Jesus molded onto it. I go straight to the pulpit, where the Preacher stands. There is nobody else to plead. I ask Jesus not to listen to everything He hears, but to me only.

Then I tell Him how it feels to be ugly, with nothing to look back at you but a deer or an owl. I read him my paper, out loud, full of His own words.

"I have been praising you, Lord, but it gets harder every year." Maybe that sounds too strong. I try to ease up my tone before the Amens. Then the chapel is very quiet. For one minute I hear the whir of many wings, but it's only a fan inside an air vent.

I go into the streets of Tulsa, where even the shade from a building is hot. And as I walk to the hotel I'm repeating, over and over, "Praise God for Tulsa in spite of everything."

Maybe I say this aloud, since people are staring. But maybe that's only because they've never seen a girl cry crooked in their streets before.

Monday morning. I have not looked at my face since the pulpit prayer. Who can predict how He might act—with a lightning bolt? Or a melting so slow and tender it could not even be felt?

Now, on the bus, I can touch in my pocketbook the cold mirror glass. Though I cover its surface with prints, I never look down. We ride through the dust and I'm nervous. My pencil is flying: "Be ye therefore perfect as your Heavenly Father is perfect. Praise God for Oklahoma. For Wagoner and Sapulpa and Broken Arrow and every other name on these signs by the road."

Was that the wrong thing to tell Him? My threat that even praise can be withheld? Maybe He's angry. "Praise God for oil towers whether I like them or not." When we pass churches I copy their names. Praise them all. I want to write, "Bless," but that's *His* job.

We cross the cool Arkansas River. As its damp rises into the bus and touches my face something wavers there, in the very bottom of each pore; and I clap my rough hands to each cheek. Maybe He's started? How much can He do between here and Fort Smith? If He will?

For I know what will happen. Monty won't come. And I won't stop. That's an end to it.

No, Monty is there. Waiting right now. And I'll go into the bus station on tiptoe and stand behind him. He'll turn, with his blue eyes like lamps. *And he won't know me!* If I'm changed. So I will explain myself to him: how this gypsy hair and this juicy mouth is still Violet Karl. He'll say, "Won't old Flick be surprised?" He'll say, "Where is that place you live? Can I come there?"

But if, while I wait and he turns, he should know me by my old face . . . If he should say my name or show by recognition that it's rising up now in his eyes like something through water . . . I'll be running by

then. To the bus. Straight out that door to the Tennessee bus, saying, "Driver, don't let that man on!" It's a very short stop. We'll be pulling out quick. I don't think he'll follow, anyhow.

I don't even think he will come.

One hundred and thirty-one miles to Fort Smith. I wish I could eat.

I try to think up things to look forward to at home. Maybe the sourwoods are blooming early, and the bees have been laying-by my honey. If it's rained enough, my corn might be in tassel. Wouldn't it be something if God took His own sweet time, and I lived on that slope for years and years, getting prettier all the time? And nobody to know?

It takes nearly years and years to get to Fort Smith. My Papa knew things about Time. I comb out my hair, not looking once to see what color sheddings are caught in the teeth. There's no need feeling my cheek, since my finger expects that scar. I can feel it on me almost anywhere, by memory. I straighten my skirt and lick my lips till the spit runs out.

And they're waiting. Monty at one door of the terminal and Flick at another.

"Ten minutes," the driver says when the bus is parked, but I wait in my seat till Flick gets restless and walks to the cigarette machine. Then I slip through his entrance door and inside the station. Mirrors shine everywhere. On the vending machines and the weight machines and a full-length one by the phone booth. It's all I can do not to look. I pass the ticket window and there's Monty's back at the other door. My face remembers the shape of it. Seeing him there, how he's made, and the parts of him fitted, makes me forget how I look. And before I can stop, I call out his name.

Right away, turning, he yells to me "VIIII—lut!"

So I know. I can look, then, in the wide mirror over a jukebox. Tired as I am and unfed, I look worse than I did when I started from home.

He's laughing and talking. "I been waiting here since daylight scared you wouldn't . . ." but by then I've run past the ugly girl in the glass and I race for the bus, for the road, for the mountain.

Behind me he calls loudly, "Flick!"

I see that one step in my path like a floating dark blade, but I'm faster this time. I twist by him, into the flaming sun and the parking lot. How my breath hurts!

Monty's between me and my bus, but there's time. I circle the cab stand, running hard over the asphalt field, with a pain ticking in my side. He calls me. I plunge through the crowd like a deer through fetterbush. But he's running as hard as he can and he's faster than me. And oh!

Praise God!

He's catching me!

THE GREYHOUND MINSTREL

By Edward Minus

Our host is Wm. Tiny. There is a rest room in the rear for our convenience. We may smoke cigarettes but pipes and cigars are not allowed. We are not to talk with Mr. Tiny while the coach is in motion. The coach is in motion.

It is after nine o'clock on a summer night, and we are traveling through a desolate and tranquil countryside. There is a moon and we can distinguish fields of corn from fields of grain, and fields of grain from fallow fields of broomstraw and milkweed. There are very few houses in sight, and most of them are dark. On the horizon, massive, light-colored clouds are waiting.

Two rows in front of me and across the aisle there is a boy, about nine or ten, with cheeks as fat as a hamster's. I noticed him and the man beside him when I first got on. The boy is dressed in a blue uniform with an emblem on one sleeve and with yellow cord trim around the collar and at the pockets and on the cap (which he is now wearing on his knee). His red hair is cut so short that it looks like the fur on a teddy bear. All I can see of him now, from here, is his left elbow and left knee, but his every word is audible to most of us on the bus. He is one of those children whose voices (tone, volume, phrasing) sound like unconscious parrotings of their mothers.

"Let me see now. Okay; I have another one. What's orange and goes click-click?"

On the boy's right, next to the window, is a thin young man with sunken cheeks and temples, a Negro, who is also in a uniform of sorts: a snug black sport jacket, a pink shirt, and a narrow black tie with a pink stripe down the middle. I cannot see his shoes, but they are certain to be the crushed-looking kind with sharply pointed toes.

"I don't believe I know," the Negro says.

"A ballpoint carrot." The boy pauses for a response that doesn't come. "Okay; I have another one for you. What's yellow, and weighs a thousand pounds, and sings, and has four legs?"

The young man waits a moment, out of respect it would seem for the difficulty of this riddle, before he says again, in the same tone, "I don't believe I know."

"Are you sure?" the boy says. "Make a guess."

"I can't guess it," the Negro tells him.

"Two five-hundred-pound canaries."

This time the young man's hesitation is more puzzled than respectful. "Now *what*?" he says.

"Two . . . five-hundred-pound . . . canaries." In a voice weary with patience. "Okay. Let me think now. Okay: This is an old one. What's the difference between the North Pole and the South Pole?"

The young man doesn't answer.

"I'm sure you know that one," the boys says.

"No. I don't believe I do."

"Do you give up?"

The young man doesn't answer.

"I said, 'Do you give up?'"

"All right," the Negro says.

"All the difference in the world," the boy declares. "See? All the difference in the *world*. You get it, don't you?"

The young man says "Yes." Then he turns to the window. I can see only the back of his head, the fine charcoal dust of his hair.

I turn toward the window on my side; toward the darkness.

Yesterday morning my father telephoned to tell me that Jimmy Bowden, my closest friend when we were growing up, had been discovered in a hotel room in Charleston, where he had killed himself by holding a plastic bag over his face. That is why I am going home: to attend the funeral tomorrow morning. I keep asking myself why I was not more shocked by the news of Jimmy's death; for the submissiveness of my response disturbs me almost as much as the tragedy itself. We were great friends from childhood through high school; and although I had seen Jimmy only twice since his marriage three years ago (when he was a sophomore in college), I had heard from him often, directly or indirectly, and I had had no reason to suspect that he and his family were not well and happy. I keep thinking now of his young wife and of his daughter and his son. I keep trying to recall the details of our last brief reunion. It was late last summer; I had just returned to this country, and on my way to Atlanta I had stopped in Enfield for several days. Jimmy and Martha asked me over for dinner one night. They had just moved into a small house on Miller Street, less than three blocks from the house where Jimmy was born. They were both full of plans that night, and their future seemed full of promise.

When I arrived they were trying to decide which of Martha's watercolors to have framed and where they should be hung. They had eight or ten of them laid out on the living room rug, most of them cool, delicate studies of wildflowers . . .

The man beside me, whose upper arm presses against mine and whose hip is hard against my hip, suddenly whimpers in his sleep. He shifts his body toward the window for an instant and then leans against me again, even more heavily than before. He has been asleep ever since I got on. His breathing is harsh and uneven; he makes constant small sucking noises in his mouth; and he sometimes moans as if in pain.

I turn toward the couple just opposite me, but they don't seem to have heard the man's whimpering. They are reading a comic book to each other. They are husband and wife, I'm sure; but both are very young, not yet twenty I would guess. The young man sits with his back to the window, his feet (in white socks) on the seat, his legs drawn up against his body so that his knees are just under his chin. The girl is curled up facing him, halfway sitting on her legs. My view is of her back, her calves and ankles, and the soles of her feet. She is also wearing white socks; her shoes are on the floor beside her husband's. Where her heel is, where the ball of her foot comes, and under the toes, the socks are grimy, almost black; but the fine high arch of her foot is still clean and white. Her legs are brown and the calves are full and hard. She is wearing a thin white blouse that buttons down the back, and when she moves a certain way the cloth gapes open between the buttons all the way down, showing a chainlike pattern of smooth brown skin.

The young man holds the comic book between them; he reads a page and then she reads a page. They

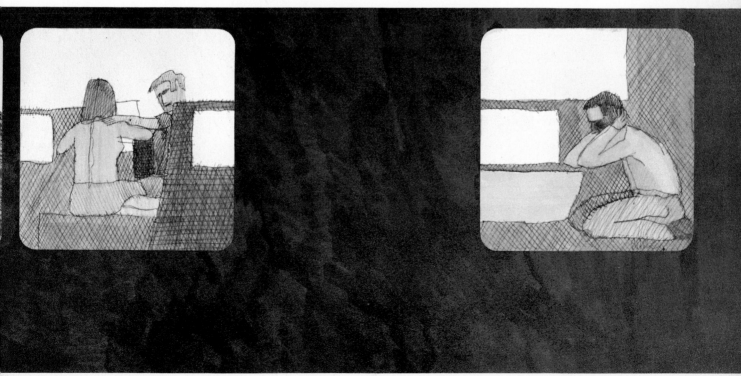

Illustrated by Wes McClure

have turned on both tiny spotlights, and he must tilt the book back and forth so that each in turn can see. The young man's voice is nasal and he reads haltingly; sometimes he spells a word and the girl pronounces it for him. Her voice is lovely, clear and tender. She is reading at the moment. The story—in which they both seem completely caught up—involves a savage African tribe and a priceless ruby—the Blood Ruby. Phrases like "the goddess of Bethlana," "mystic spell," and "magic potion" recur with great frequency. The girl's light brown hair is pinned up in the back, exposing the nape of her neck; and as she reads her husband lays his arm across her shoulder and with the tips of his fingers gently strokes the slight furrow at the base of her skull, where her hair is soft and shining.

As I listen to the girl's voice, I become aware that one part of my mind has been quietly reconstructing, making inventory as it were, the house where Jimmy and his family lived when we were in grade school: recalling the floor plan, the doorways and windows, the position of each piece of furniture, the color and texture of the carpets. I remember most clearly a picture that hung over the sideboard in the Bowdens' dining room, a large, beautifully framed oil painting of a magnificent oak tree, a tree that seemed made for climbing, a tree of massive limbs and luxuriant foliage, casting a purple shade. That picture, that tree—although it sometimes made me think of a thundercloud—that tree seemed to give form to the feeling of strength and peace that I was often so poignantly and so gratefully aware of in Jimmy's home, among his family, so unlike my own. I used to have a dream in which Jimmy and I were climbing in that tree . . .

Near the front of the bus a baby begins to cry fretfully. The man beside me, with what seems a terrible effort, leans his body away from mine; he straightens his back and presses his shoulders and the back of his head against the seat. I glance toward him and see that he is awake. He is rubbing his hand over his jaw and across his mouth. His breathing is heavy and he seems almost to be moaning under his breath. A moment later he bends forward until his head nearly touches the seat in front of him. He dangles one arm between his legs. He finds a small paper cup on the floor at his feet and leans back again. He puts the cup to his mouth.

"Now listen," the moon-faced boy is saying. "This is a funny one. So now listen. What's the difference between an elephant and a grape?"

The young man looks out the window; the boy leans forward.

"What's the difference between an elephant and a grape?" he says again.

The Negro shakes his head.

The boy feigns incredulity. "You don't know *any* difference between an *elephant* and a *grape*?"

"They's lots of differences," the Negro says.

"A grape's purple," the boy tells him. "Now: You know what Tarzan said when he saw the elephants coming?"

The young man shakes his head.

"You do know who Tarzan is, don't you?"

"Yeah. Sure."

"Do you know what he said when he saw the elephants coming?"

"I said I didn't."

"He said, 'Here come the grapes.' He was color-blind." For the first time the boy laughs out loud. His laughter is light and infectious. The two young women who are sitting behind him begin to laugh too. The Negro turns and gives the boy a quick, angry look.

At the front of the bus a soldier stands up and heads down the aisle, holding on to the seats with both hands to keep his balance. There is something ursine about the set of his shoulders and the sleepy way he moves, but his sunburned face looks kind and intelligent. He goes into the washroom at the end of the aisle. When I boarded the bus, this soldier and another one were sleeping soundly in the seats just behind the driver. One slept with his cheek pressed against the window, and the other one slept with his head on his companion's shoulder. Their mouths were open and their knees were spread apart; their hands lay limp and gracefully cupped between their thighs.

The man beside me is speaking to me, but I cannot understand what he is saying. I lean toward him, and he repeats his question, but the words are terribly blurred and garbled. At first I thought that he was speaking a foreign language; now it occurs to me that perhaps he is drunk. "I'm sorry," I say to him, leaning even closer. When he repeats the question a third time, I realize that he is asking where I'm going. "Enfield," I tell him; "I'm on my way to Enfield." I want to keep talking in order to put off more questions, but I can think of nothing to say to him. I do not want to mention the reason I am going home. I am afraid that if I did tell him he would not understand; and the thought of trying to explain, the thought of having to say it all over again, brings on an acute sadness.

He puts the small paper cup to his mouth. For a time I thought that he was drinking from it, but he is spitting into it. He continues to make small sucking noises in his mouth. Now he is speaking again; but I cannot understand him. I turn so that I can watch his lips. The words come once more; but despite the effort they cost him, they are not words, only noises, ugly and senseless. He says them again, and again, while I nod at him stupidly. At last, miraculously, the sounds become more than a dreadful babbling: "I been on this dog all day long," he is saying. He coughs and spits into the cup. He is an old man with sour breath. His face is bloated; the sallow, unshaven flesh looks like a thick rubber mask, behind which his eyes are dry and vacant. The backs of his hands are mapped with chocolate-colored islands. He is wearing a black suit of a hard and heavy material and a white shirt that is badly wrinkled. Now that he has finally gotten through to me, he leans back with a sigh that is almost a whimper and closes his eyes.

Across the aisle, the husband is reading; he has moved his hand from the girl's neck to her thigh. I want terribly to reach out and touch that shallow spot at her hairline, where his blunt fingers have been stroking. I feel an aching desire to grasp her foot and hold it tight, pressing my thumb into the high, firm arch. If only the husband would go to sleep. He turns the page and the girl begins to read.

Through the window beside the old man, and through the dim reflection there of the young couple reading their comic book, I can see that we are passing a large open field, bordered by black woods. I close my eyes and think of the times when Jimmy and I went hunting together. How many such fields we sauntered across in the rose-colored late afternoons in the autumn. And how many early mornings we sat huddled in the icy darkness, deep in the thickets beside the lake, waiting for the ducks to come in . . .

A teasing fragment of a seldom heard song distracts my memory. Near the back of the bus there is a Negro woman with a transistor radio, which she plays constantly. She does not care for news programs, weather reports, interviews, or commercials—only music; and she seems to be searching, sometimes almost frantically, for one particular song—she listens to a single station for no more than five or ten minutes at a time. And in the process of changing from one station to another, she is always compelled to explore the entire dial. About an hour ago she happened on a station that promised three hours of uninterrupted music, but halfway through a tremulous rendition of "Soon," the needle stuck at the words "climate is," which were then repeated over and over again: "climate is—, climate is—, climate is— climate is—." Now, each time the woman scans the dial, she pauses at that spot, sometimes for a minute or more: "climate is—, climate is—, climate is—, climate is—." It's as if the two words have her mesmerized. Or perhaps she has reason to believe that the very next song on that record is the one she is longing to hear. For the moment she has settled for a sleazy instrumental: "Stars are falling on Alabama."

The young Negro man says, "In a rabbit gum, I reckon."

"There's an even better way," the moon-faced boy tells him.

The young man says nothing.

"Do you know what it is?"

"No," the Negro says.

"You're supposed to say, 'I give up.'"

"All right," the Negro says.

"Do you give up?"

"All right."

"Hide behind a tree and make a noise like a carrot." The boy starts laughing again, but he stops abruptly. "Okay," he says, "I'll give you a real easy one this time. What's black and white and red all over?"

The young man says nothing, and the boy waits.

I can't for-get the glam-our: / My arms wound around you tight.

"A newspaper," the young man says.

"No!" the boy shouts. "An embarrassed zebra!" Another spasm of laughter follows, and again the two young women join in.

The old man puts the small white cup to his mouth. Involuntarily, I turn to look at him. There is something almost imbecilic about the slackness of the lower part of his face; his lips and his chin are trembling, and his mouth gapes open as if his tongue is terribly swollen. He begins to talk again. The tone and the cadence of his voice, and the dark lines that cross his forehead, convey a troubled urgency. But the sounds that come out of his mouth are a travesty of speech. Like his face, they are slack and flaccid; they are as empty of meaning as his eyes, and they are so distorted that they sound scarcely human. And yet, the more he talks, the less difficult it becomes to understand what he is trying to say. More often, and more readily, the repellent noises resemble words, and the words fit together. He watches me closely, and when I frown even slightly he repeats what he has said.

I learn that his home is in Taylors, a small town some fifteen or twenty miles beyond Enfield. He caught a bus there this morning at 4:30 and arrived in Columbia shortly after nine. It seems that there is a dental clinic of sorts in Columbia where teeth are extracted at the rate of a dollar a tooth, and where false teeth may be purchsed for an equally nominal sum. Between ten and two Mr. Harnes (Harves? Hartz?) had all his teeth pulled and impressions made for upper and lower plates, which will be mailed to him next week. The important thing is—Mr. Harnes seems especially proud of this fact and keeps coming back to it—he has had to miss only one day of work.

His gums are still bleeding, of course—he apologizes again and again for his continual spitting—and he says that he still feels "doped up." Except for a bowl of soup, he has had nothing to eat since early morning. He tries to tell me something about his wife: I believe he is saying that she, too, plans to undergo this ordeal as soon as they can afford it. There is something else—about a telephone call, but I cannot at all grasp the details of this matter, nor determine the reason the old man is so troubled about it; and, at last, the effort of getting through to me tires him into silence. Even as he talked, he continued to spit into the cup after every sentence or so; and I begin to wonder how much blood he must have swallowed while asleep, and how much more the cup will hold now, how often he has to empty it. I suddenly realize that the soldier has not yet returned from the rest room. I lean into the aisle and look toward the front to make sure he has not gone by without my noticing. His seat is empty. It seems a good half hour since he went back; and it occurs to me that he may be ill, may even have fainted, and that someone should see about him. But then again—perhaps he is in there masturbating. Or drawing obscene pictures on the walls.

I remember, for the first time in many years, what Jimmy used to write on the walls in the rest rooms at school and at the Center Theatre, and on his desks, and in the backs of library books. He always used to write one thing: "I love pussy." Only he used to put a lot of "o's" in "love": "I loooooove pussy." Wherever you saw that, you knew Jimmy had been there.

When we first knew each other, there was something almost comic about Jimmy's appearance. He kept his hair cut short, which made his long face look even longer; and his slightly angular features were always surprisingly mobile. But by the time we got to high school, his face had taken shape and his features had settled into a solemn handsomeness. All through high school I envied his good looks and his girls and his way with girls. It was impossible, though, for me to be like him, and the next best thing—or perhaps it was just as good; almost the same in a way—was to be his close friend . . .

The man beside me stirs and whimpers as he begins to fall asleep again. A couple of seats behind me, two young girls (twelve or thirteen, I suppose) have put aside their movie magazines and are playing a game called Favorites.

"Drink," one of them says.

"Cherry-Coke."

"Iced tea with mint," says the first.

"Color," the other one says.

"Lime."

"Grey."

"Teacher."

"All through school or just this year?"

"All through school."

"Miss Propes."

"Mrs. James."

"Month."

"July."

"December."

"Sport to watch."

"Football."

"Basketball."

"Boy's name."

"Jerry."

"Me too: Jerry." They begin to giggle.

The soldier comes out of the rest room and makes his way back to his seat. Near the front of the bus the baby begins to cry, but once again the mother quiets him very quickly.

"You still can't think of any?" the moon-faced boy says.

"I don't believe so," the Negro says. He is looking out the window again. He has turned his whole body, so that only his right arm and shoulder are against the back of the seat.

"It's not as much fun when I have to do all the asking," the boy complains. "Do you know any jokes?"

The Negro shakes his head.

"Not any you can tell me, huh?"

"That's right," the Negro says.

The boy says, "You wanta hear the dirtiest joke I know?"

"Not specially," the Negro murmurs.

"Okay. If you really wanta hear it. There was this beautiful snow-white horse galloping down the road, and it slipped and fell in a mud hole. That's the dirtiest joke I know."

This time the two young women laugh, but the boy does not; he is busy thinking.

"What has wheels and cuts grass and lives in a tree?" he says.

The young man says nothing.

"Do you give up?"

The Negro nods his head.

"A lawnmower," the boy says. "I was lying when I said it lived in a tree."

The couple on my right have finished one comic book and are about to start another. They have half a dozen or more tucked into the pockets on the backs of the seats in front of them. On the cover of one of the books there is a picture of a doctor and a nurse in a passionate embrace; but the girl has chosen one called "Monsters of Tomorrow." She has not yet opened it; she is reading every word on the cover, front and back; the back is devoted to an advertisement for Christmas cards. Out of the corner of my eye I watch the husband's hand move from her calf to her thigh, and then disappear. My own hands are tingling, throbbing. I imagine undoing the buttons of her blouse and slowly folding back the panels of cloth, and then unfastening the brassiere. I press the palms of my hands against her shoulder blades, and then smooth my hands down to the small of her back; my fingertips snag the top of her pants and I slowly peel them down the swell of her buttocks. I turn away, but her reflection is in the window. I see that someone has left a pulp magazine in the pocket on the back of the seat in front of me. I take it out and turn on the small light above my seat. Inside the magazine there is a folded piece of ruled tablet paper, a letter, written in pencil:

Dear Don,

I have got some real bad news to tell you, we have had a terrible accident. I no that you told me not to write to you again but Donnie is your son as much as he is mine and mama says you ought to be told what has happen to him. Mama was staying with him last night while I went out and when she took her eyes off him for a min. he pulled a pan of boiling hot water off the stove. He got burned real bad on his face and all on his little chest and arms and the drs. don't know wether he will live or die. I just no that if he dies I will want to die too and mama feels that same way too. All we can do is pray that God will have mercy on him and will not make him suffer for what you and me did to each other. I don't know wether this letter will reach you or not but mama said you ought to know what happen to him since he is your own son and we hope that you will pray for him. He is in the Chester hospital. We still live on Randall St.

> Your wife,
> Shirlene

I put the letter and the magazine back into the pocket. As I push myself up out of the seat, I feel a sharp, sudden pain behind my eyes, and I hear myself gasp. The old man wakes and says something to me that I cannot understand. I start down the aisle, groping at the seats in order to steady myself.

"Chocolate parfait," says one little girl.

"Strawberry shortcake," says the other one.

"Climate is—, climate is—, climate is—, climate is—"

I lock the rest room door and lean back against it. The noise and the motion of the bus seem far greater, more erratic in here. I look at myself in the mirror; my face seems almost unfamiliar, not at all like Jimmy's. There is a sign on the lavatory that says, "This water is not for drinking." On the front wall of the compartment there is a small red button labelled "In case of emergency." The pain comes again, more brutal than before, and I feel that I am going to vomit. I get down on the floor, my knees straddling the small metal toilet. Bracing one hand against the wall and holding on to the rim of the bowl with the other, I look down into the small black hole, which seems to be roaring and spinning and sucking. I try to remember. I try to remember . . .

My fingers begin to ache. I suddenly realize how very long I have been kneeling here, wanting to vomit; I am surprised and hurt that no one has come back to see about me.

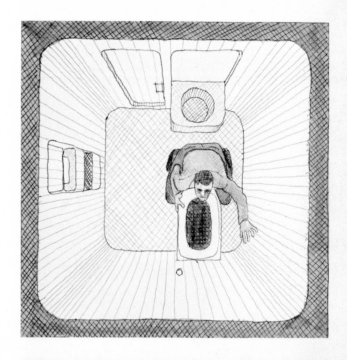

RENATA: IT'S REALLY YOU

By James Mechem

Renata, darling, it's you. Very pretty. I have your smile in my heart. I love you, your pearly teeth, oily lashes, dimples, snub nose, forehead, broad face. Yes, Renata.

It's really you, darling.

I don't care, darling.

I want you.

You've just turned forty-five.

I'll be forty-four in ten months. Your nose turns up like mine.

I used to have a mustache that turned up but I don't any more. It was patterned after Salvador Dali's. I saw a picture of you tweaking his mustache.

I lack half an inch of being six feet, which must be your height in heels. I think you have blue eyes and brown hair which is what I have.

I knew it was you by your high forehead, dimples, pearly teeth and snub nose. The likeness struck me with the force of conviction and I said "Renata—it's really you."

It was in the summertime in Rome and it was hot. Renata was recording. Every day after rehearsing and recording Renata would walk from the studio to her hotel. I am an American and do not speak Italian. I recognized Renata by her picture. I wanted to walk with her and without thinking about it I walked up to her and smiled and fell into step with her. She was in flat shoes and I found, as I have always imagined, that I was a little taller than she. I am telling you now what happened on the first day. Shall I say it was today? After today I shall record what happens without knowing what's going to happen, unless something else happens, unless my pages get shuffled, unless my imagination takes over. As I say, I found I was a little taller than Renata. I know she speaks English but she said nothing. She smiled at me and I fell into step with her. I was bolder by walking up to her than I could have been if I had thought about it, particularly since I don't speak Italian. I thought I was doing something extremely foolhardy when I was walking across the street to her. I had recognized her

from the other side of the street. She saw me crossing to her. I didn't take my eyes off her. She had never seen me before as far as I know. I don't know when she could have. As I say, I am an American in Rome. My heart was in my throat. But I couldn't stop walking toward her. I didn't know what was going to happen. Something dire. But I couldn't stop. Now she was waiting for me, her eyes in mine as I approached, returning my smile. I did not take my eyes from her face but as I reached the curb I touched her elbow and turned with her to walk. She turned easily. Then we were walking together.

I was not dressed like a tramp. I had a fresh haircut, manicure, and my shoes were shined. I like to keep up my appearance. I don't like to go out unpressed. I spend a lot of money on my clothes. I seldom ever look like a tramp. I have the look of a professional man, which of course I am.

Naturally I was bothered by the traffic as I crossed— I had to depend on side vision because I could not take my eyes off her. I don't know how close I came to being hit. I wish I could see a movie of myself crossing the street. I probably had some shaves without knowing. Oh, I knew it; it was all distracting me very much, because I was so uneasy to begin with about approaching Renata—because I didn't know what I would say—even in English. When I got to the curb and I was face to face with Renata I said nothing. And if for a moment there was a question in her expression it was only for a fleeting moment, because she accepted me at once and turned with me, saying nothing.

At the door of her hotel I touched her elbow again. I did not want to break the silence. We had walked four blocks in the hot Roman evening without speaking. More than anything in the world I wanted to say nothing, to keep the silence between us. I touched her shoulders with both hands and ducked my head just barely brushing her left cheek in a phantom embrace. I smiled and walked on. We had not said a word. She said nothing now. She only smiled and went

Illustrated by Ken Hidgon

into her hotel and I walked on out of the light of the hotel and discovered that night had fallen.

Renata fainted at the sight of her smashed dolls— the dolls that had been given to her all through her career and that she carried with her everywhere . . . Violetta, Mimi, Tosca . . . all the roles she had sung.

Her doctor was there when she came to, and the police and her personal assistant and her secretary.

In one week she was scheduled to open the new season. This seemed designed to keep her from it. Why else would anyone break into her room and do this?

She did not have the strength to get off her bed.

She wished for the discipline that everyone attributed to her and which she herself felt she lacked.

As soon as the police and the doctor were gone she cried without control.

When she was a little girl she had taken her doll to

school—the only thing in the world that was all her own—and it had been broken. Now as a world famous diva she was suffering a similar blow.

I didn't see her yesterday because I wasn't able to be there on time, but today I was. She smiled as soon as she saw me. I was waiting for her outside the studio and when she saw me she walked toward me smiling with her eyes and mouth. I liked her very much in that moment.

When she first stepped out I saw her eyes searching in the dim light of Rome at evening. Then when she saw me she nodded and then her face changed to a smile and she hurried toward me.

Naturally I was smiling from ear to ear because I was happy to see her again, happy that she recognized me and happy that she came up to me like that. I wanted very much to be with her for these few minutes that it took us to walk from her studio to her hotel. I said nothing. It had been pleasant yesterday—no, it was the day before yesterday—walking with her in silence and I was hoping that she would say nothing.

She was evidently not going to speak because she smiled only and turned to walk to her hotel, confident that I was going that way with her.

It made me very pleased and proud to walk beside her and guide her through the traffic.

She knows nothing of me, probably. My photograph is not so publicized as hers. Undoubtedly she knows that I know her.

I'm content to meet her every day like this. I think the moment one of us breaks the silence something will be lost.

She is very nice to look at. The night has begun to settle but the way to her hotel is lighted since it is busy with traffic and commerce as you must know.

There's no telling what she thinks of this but she can't find it unattractive or she would not have smiled with such sincerity last night when she left me—I'm sorry—two nights ago. She smiled this evening when she saw me and knew that I was waiting for her.

Renata probably knows I am not Italian. She probably knows I am American. I don't know but I fancy she does. Every minute I am with her I am more pleased with sharing the world for a quarter of an hour with her. Whenever I think of it, and I almost never stop, it seems surprising, even strange and not a little unreal.

I look at her now and smile. I wonder if she shares the same fear that I will break the silence. I really believe that as soon as we introduce ourselves everything is over.

Therefore I cannot say "Good evening," "Good night" "Thank you," or "I love you."

Perhaps she is feeling none of this. But when I left her at her hotel she winked at me and walked in.

"I fainted."

"About what time was that, Signorina?"

"Late morning. That's all I know."

"It's noon now," the police sergeant said.

They stayed about half an hour.

There are three Renatas. The one I am writing about; the one I dream about from the photographs I have; and the real Renata Tebaldi. I know little about Signorina Tebaldi; the one I am dreaming about is too romantic to let you see; and the one I am writing about seems too fictitious. Nevertheless she is the only one I can show you.

I put myself into the story as a romantic lead, an American script writer and director of artistic films (I wish I were). I shall arrange to meet Renata. I hope that she falls in love with me.

This is my favorite form of writing. In the past I have written myself into love stories with Eileen Farrell, Geraldine Page, Hortense Calisher, and Francoise Mallet-Joris.

It was not she who did not show up the next day. It was me. I have been busy. I haven't been able to meet her for three days. But when she stepped out today and saw me and smiled I knew how much I had missed her.

There was the delight of recognition in her eyes. For a moment I thought she was going to say something and I almost wanted her to.

We walked six blocks past her hotel without stopping and at the same instant turned back. Renata put her arm in mine and we walked back to her hotel without a word (naturally).

When Renata returned to her hotel someone had smashed her dolls. It was the worst possible calamity! She fainted. Her personal assistant helped to bring her to. The police were there. Renata stood up and began to yell at the police with total unconcern for the damage she was doing to her voice. She was scheduled to open the opera season next week—but all this was impossible now!

Everything was impossible except her own survival. How would she live now? Struck down at the peak of her career. No! She wasn't through yet. She told the police quietly to leave and she called her doctor. But the damage was done. Her voice was gone. It would take three weeks to recover from the strain she had given it.

The papers played it up. The director of the opera house arrived. She whispered that she was going to sing. She saw he didn't believe her and she screamed at him to get out and then regretted it. He was followed that morning by her understudy. That was the last straw!

I went to met Renata today even though I had a headache. I can't have been very good company. The pain was probably showing in my eyes. I doped myself up with aspirin before I left but it didn't seem to do any good.

Renata left the meeting with the new movie writer in despondency. She couldn't explain the sadness that now gripped her heart.

She wanted to be silent and alone. She paid the driver and entered her hotel. Her secretary and personal assistant had gone to a movie and the apartment was quiet when she entered. She lay down but did not close her eyes. Her depression had vanished. She was content. Something new was happening. She hadn't felt like this before. She slipped off her shoes and let them drop on the floor and turned on her stomach, chin propped up, thinking hard—about nothing. She was being lazy. She was suddenly happy. She opened her eyes wide and looked round in the half-dark.

Though not her own, the room was satisfying and familiar suddenly. She didn't dare move. She continued to stare with her chin on her elbow, meditating, alert to her shifting moods, wondering how justified she was in letting herself become so romantic over pure laziness. She got up and walked out of the bedroom. She was impatient for company, restless, bored.

What was happening to her? She was just a little frightened. She felt stimulated as though after a party. Her heart was racing. She was so dizzy she was forced to sit down. Was she ill? She disciplined herself to sit patiently for some minutes. There was nothing wrong with her. Sometimes her heart acted like this. It was not unusual. She was herself again. She began to think about the rehearsal and recording she would do tomorrow.

"I'm afraid this writer is going to be a nuisance," she thought. She would like him to write his movie and leave her alone. Tomorrow she would tell him: "Just write your movie. That's what you're here for. Follow the outline I gave you. Don't bother me more than you have to."

The movie and the American threatened her. They could too easily take up too much of her time and energy. "That's why you're here," she would say. "To take the work on by yourself. I thought you wrote the script of a movie entered in the Cannes Film Festival?"

She had been aware of his name for several years. She knew he was not well known in America. This had surprised her when she first read his translated pieces.

If she had never seen his movie he would not be here now and she would not be in this predicament. The last thing she wanted to do was make a movie. He was here one day and she was tired of the whole idea. He didn't speak a word of Italian.

Would she shoot it in Italian as planned or dub the Italian afterward? The problems were already insurmountable. She didn't have time to worry about them.

Let him worry. That's what he was here for. She had too much else to do.

She was very much attracted to the American without knowing what the source of the attraction was. His name was not well known. He was not wealthy. He did not speak Italian.

But in his favor, he dressed nicely. He was tall and dark and very good looking with a fair skin. His writing had something different to it. He was unlike anybody in the world. Extremely original. He was unmarried.

He had a stubborn streak in him. She couldn't push him around. He had written the script in a week and was now taking charge of the movie. Instead of being a nuisance by taking up too much of her time he was doing just the opposite, becoming frankly independent with her money and her movie. He had stolen her secretary and was using her as an interpreter for movie business, then for personal business.

She went to see how the movie was going. They were shooting outside the city. She paid the driver and dismissed him. Almost as soon as she got out of the cab he came walking to her looking a trifle cold in the wind but dressed smartly as usual.

He walked back to the set with her. "We're just finishing," he said. "This one last scene and then we're through for the day."

She nodded at her secretary who was coming to meet them. Miss Angelo was a trim woman with a dark face. Her eyeglass frames were heavy, the lenses thick. Renata shook hands with her cameraman, Julius Caseli, and her director, Decamo Martelli.

The American, Alfred Farrell, had assumed the duties of producer's assistant. She was pleased at herself for hiring him in the way she did. He was what they called in the American westerns "the ramrod." He got things going and kept them running.

She rode back into Rome with him.

The next afternoon he called to tell her they were going to start shooting her in the morning.

"You don't have any real conflict for two months. I checked. If we shoot straight through I think we can get finished in time for the Tokyo Film Festival. I'm so sure of it I've had your secretary reserve a berth on a ship and a hotel on the Ginza."

"Yes, you are pretty sure." She hung up.

Today again I am waiting outside her studio as the sun is setting as Renata steps out and sees me with the sun full in my face.

NO BOUNDARIES AT ALL

By Laurel Trivelpiece

He exists without limits, without a name. Oh, he must know his name—sometimes Rosemary is convinced he knows his name! At certain times he turns his head when she calls, "Jerome, Jerome!" This point fastens on her often at the darkest moments, those three o'clock in the mornings moments, when she opens the medicine cabinet for a second sleeping pill. He must have at least an intermittent grasp of his name. She swallows the capsule, and her rising panic, without water. He cannot exist down there completely exposed, with no boundaries at all!

Rosemary is fifteen pounds underweight. Since the day at nursery school three months ago the brown crescents of shadow under her eyes have deepened so much her face has a piebald look. As she slips back into bed she curves herself into her husband's sleeping warmth. At least we lean on each other, she thinks, and thinks of the times each has leaned and the other was not there. Sometimes the first light of morning is lifting the shadows around the curtains before the second sleeping pill works. But within the hour Jerome will wake up, and so must she. For a few days or weeks longer; she does not think about what happens after that.

This morning he is throwing blocks at his locked door, and his sleepers are leaking as usual. Rosemary uses three double night diapers, but he is almost four now. Tall and decidedly thin; even if one did not see his eyes one would sense something wrong. Jerome's head is too long from back to forehead.

Illustrated by E. D. Guest

His hair is a beige plush that shows his narrow skull underneath. Rosemary and Clyde can manage only a patchy butch cut. Of course a trip to the barber has never been seriously considered. These days Rosemary's mouth shakes when she first sees her son in the morning. Jerome looks through her with his hollow blue eyes.

Breakfast is done in shifts. While Rosemary somehow applies dry clothes to Jerome, Clyde fills his bottle, makes the coffee, starts the eggs and toast. Then he comes in to watch Jerome, and if possible, change the bed and get the washing machine loaded while Rosemary drinks her coffee. They shout back and forth.

"And gin," Rosemary often calls. "I forgot to put it on your list."

Clyde calls back from the hall where he is piling wet sheets in the machine. "He got out! Watch it—living room!" They almost collide as they rush in but they are too late. Jerome is huddled in his favorite refuge, the fireplace, and there are ashes all over the rug. The trick now is to move in slowly, smoothly; they must overpower him imperceptibly like a tide.

"What did you do—what brought this on?" Rosemary whispers and Clyde whispers back, "Do! Since when did anyone have to do anything? Now. I'm going for his feet." Jerome and more ashes are pulled from the fireplace, and all three, long practiced, move toward the bathroom.

"God damn it, I'll be late again," Clyde says, but without anger. He runs the bath while Rosemary strips off the ashy clothes. Jerome stands still, waiting. "And he didn't throw any at us this time, did you notice?" Rosemary says. "See how quietly he stands and lets Mother undress him."

"Oh, that's progress!" Clyde says. "This kid's a real comer." But Rosemary does not smile, and Clyde's eyes have that tight look they always get when he tries for the light touch. Carefully he lifts the boy into the tub. "Here, fella." He touches her face for a moment before he goes off to drink his coffee.

This life that is ending soon is as timeless as a squirrels' wheel. But sometimes Rosemary suddenly thinks: all those maternity dresses! Those foolish lists of names! Her mother wanted it to be a girl. Jennifer Rose. She had almost cried one night when Clyde had said, enjoying every word, that he had never been able to stand the name Jennifer, and was insisting on a son anyway. They'd had to play another game of Scrabble with Mother. And then Clyde got his son. Jerome. They had named him Jerome.

That was before the convulsions and the coma; the high, high screen around her bed and the round white pills that carried her over it and returned her for another white circle of horror. Clyde's stiff face, her mother's tears, and the great release Rosemary could never afford later.

"Keep her out of here—I can't stand that, too! No more, no more!" Her tears had spotted Clyde's shoulder and that was all. They were drowning in separate depths.

While her mother kept the stone floor of the cathedral across the street warm with her wide knees, the specialists moved in swiftly around Jerome's little spasm of flesh and used long, awkward words that vibrated improbably against their numbness. Rosemary and Clyde could not say those words to each other.

Later on at least they could quarrel. When it was clear that the baby would live, they had flown at each other like lovers, alive and angry. "An electric train! Oh God, the comic-strip father! Clyde, Clyde. He is sixteen months old and cannot sit alone. He cannot sit up!" Clyde had smiled anyway, how his hair and face had faded that year, and unwrapped the gaudily articulated cars and placed them gently in front of Jerome's vacant little face. He could not help bringing things; once a tiny leather baseball glove, the kind one oils. She had gone into the bathroom and wept against the painted panels of the door. In those days she was a glutinous mass of emotions. Later, she had called her mother (there had been time then for phone calls) and had listened calmly to the recital of prayers said, and candles lit, and the philosophy of Father Housener. " . . . not for us to fathom the mysteries of God . . . there is a pattern, darling, if we could see it. Rosemary, won't you, can't you . . ." She had been able to listen in those days. And later she and Clyde had made love with a silent greed that lifted them away for a little while.

She would hardly have thought so at the time, her heart moulting like a pigeon every time Jerome was in her arms, but those were the easy months. Had she never really taken in the fact that baby-sitters, soft-faced with pity, would come, for hours at a time? Those were the easy months.

For suddenly, as the doctors had predicted all along, he was sitting, and standing, and walking—and then he was in violent motion fourteen hours a day. All his waking hours he ranged and lunged as uncontrollable as a nightmare. The sitters would come no more and they could not afford special nurses. Volunteering friends did not try twice to handle him.

The electric outlets were taped shut; the stove knobs removed. "No, no! You must not step on kitty. Don't hurt kitty. My God, don't throw her!" They gave away their ten year old Betsy, thankful her bruised ribs had healed.

Rosemary's life closed down like a ring. It contained only rooms bare of furniture and a boy-shaped entity who did not see her when he looked at her. Clyde of course remained the same, still bringing home the toys, and, it was ludicrous, even books. His attempts at humor were only to please her, she knew that. But for her part she became as impersonal as a caretaker. Her baby with his still white hands and silent face was gone, and now she felt nothing at all. It was a relief. The long days that raged around them left no room for emotions, anyway. And the only feelings Jerome ever displayed were for the blanket he must have at naptime. She was just holding on until they could find a school or institution to take him. Let her mother and God worry about love, and grief, and hope. That was not her department; she had no strength for non-essentials now.

She had to take care of Jerome, she thought, as she gave him his bottle and toast (he would take almost nothing else and would eat only crouched behind the stove) and she would, but only a neurotic fool would berate herself for lacking a love that could not even be noticed, let alone returned.

Their pediatrician, Dr. Arner, patiently returned her phone calls. "He's been jumping from the table to the floor for the past three hours. The minute I let go of him he's back at it. You've got to do something!" Dr. Arner prescribed more tranquillizers that did not tranquillize and urged her to hang on a little longer. He no longer enthused about Jerome's physical progress and said it would soon be time to run another battery of tests with the consulting neurologists and clinical pychologists. "But of course, right now the best possible environment for so young a child is a one to one relationship at home. I know it's rough, and it will be six more months before Jerome has matured enough to even try to test extensively." Six more months, and they could find help, treatment, turn the problem over to experts.

Six more months to go. Rosemary discovered gin. A dose on getting up, a nip or two at canny intervals during the day. Not too much—she must be able to run and tackle, dodge and carry on the half second. Jerome now weighed thirty-five hostile pounds. He had never smiled or spoken a word. He looked right through them as though they were transparent obstacles to the destruction he must, he could *not* be stopped, he must carry out. He slips his pale, wet eyes around their sight. Jerome's eyes are too close together. He has long blue veins in his thin cheeks.

They were prisoners, she and Jerome. For six months they were to be locked together. She and Clyde no longer quarrelled or wept in each other's arms. They no longer made love. Living became very uncluttered when it demanded every shred of nerve and muscle to care for their damaged son. After Jerome went to sleep they drank heavily, silently, together and fell into bed like stones. She said once, "I don't know why people go on so about sex. As I remember it, it couldn't possibly come up to sleeping. Just lying here, still, quiet. Sleeping!" Clyde had laughed and a laugh was something. She had not needed pills then to plunge into sleep, and her heart was clear and cold when she wrenched herself out into another day. She made it a point to turn away when Clyde came home from work and slowly looked into his son's face.

At last Dr. Arner summoned them in for more con-

sultations, EEG's, pyschological tests. He always met her at the office with the hopeful smile of an accomplice. He was young but only a few black hairs were still spaced out on his tanned scalp. She was always aware of the effort he made to give her his complete attention; that, his concentration implied, was one thing he could do, at least. He patted her shoulder a lot when she got up to leave.

He had something new to tell her at the last of this series of appointments. He turned his yellow pencil around and around in his fingers and did not meet her eyes. "The thing is, he is still so young the EEG doesn't show much, although we know there must have been gross insult to the brain at birth, and that probably explains his emotional alienation and mental retardation. But whatever the reason, for practical purposes what we're up against is an autistic personality. Are you familiar with that term?" Rosemary's reading in medical texts had been wide since Jerome's birth, and the word hit her with mortal accuracy. She closed her eyes and could see the words:

"—the autistic child seems to have no sense of self; he cannot receive or extend love and affection . . . apparently regards himself as an extension of a hostile environment—"

Dr. Arner brought her a glass of water; Jerome, crouched near her shoes, reached up and tipped it in her lap. "I know how you feel, Rosemary, but you must not give up hope." Hope! she thought. Hope!

"There are schools for children like these," Dr. Orner went on. "New drugs, new therapy techniques. There are ways of helping them. And we're fortunate that right here in town is one of the best schools in the country, the Child Behavior Center. They take them at this age, and I would say let's place him there as soon as possible. Most of the children live in, and I'll be frank with you, Jerome probably will need such extensive care for a number of years. We must face that fact."

But the list of applicants at the Child Behavior Center was long. They must go home and wait some more. "Meanwhile," Dr. Arner said, he was patting her shoulder now, "try to expose him to other children. Any nursery school experience would be invaluable. Make some phone calls, explain the situation, you never know." Rosemary nodded. Autistic. An autistic child. She must phone Clyde to bring a fresh supply of gin tonight. Evidently she had thanked the doctor for she and Jerome seemed to be leaving.

He got loose from her in the waiting room and rolled in the shadows under the magazine table. She tried to keep her voice low. "Jerome, please. Please come out. You must come now." A woman was sitting on the bench with a little girl, a blond child with a profile like those stamped on coins. Both were watching closely. The woman finally spoke. "You know, I find one has to be firm. These modern ideas—"

"He is an autistic child," Rosemary said loudly and dully, leaving space between each word. She was rather startled to hear her own voice.

"Well, so is my daughter! Perfect pitch at three! But just because a child is gifted is no reason to spoil and indulge—" she went on while Rosemary bent and grabbed a dark knee and dragged Jerome to the car. She had forgotten the mother and daughter before she got the motor started. Autistic. And she would have to tell Clyde. She had never felt so tired in her life.

The next day she telephoned the nearest nursery school. The school would take him! Never mind that at three and one-half he did not speak (or smile or laugh, but she did not mention that), was not toilet-trained, and was, Rosemary explained, admiring her turn of the truth, "rather violent in his efforts to relate to other children."

The nursery school director answered in the same tongue. "The opportunities our school offers for creative growth, both as a separate individual and as a contributing member of the group, are too important to be confined to the well-adjusted. A child cannot hope to relate adequately to other children unless he is exposed, consistently, to his peer group. So often, we find, a mother is too close to her child to deal with his problems." Rosemary did not say that the closeness between zoo-keeper and wild bear might be something else again. She thanked the director evenly but she could not get the phone back on the hook until the third try. Two and one half hours every morning free of Jerome! She phoned Clyde. She phoned her mother, who, unable to bear the sight of her blighted grandson, confined the help she mentioned so often to wooing God in his behalf. Well, who knows, perhaps mother and God between them had pulled this off! Of course after the teachers saw him in action—Rosemary's chest filled with a grainy fear. She spent the rest of Jerome's all too brief naptime lying on her back and looking at the ceiling, smoking one cigarette after another.

Clyde stayed to drive them to nursery school on the appointed morning. A double ration of tranquillizers and a roll of peppermints got Jerome in the car. He sat in the back seat; pink dripping from his mouth down over his crisp shirt; his hands busy as paws pushing the candies in. Rosemary sat beside him, her hands wrenched together as if they were welded, as they drove slowly along. Only the middle of the street was visible in the crowding white morning fog.

The director, Mrs. Bradley, met them at the primary-red door. "Good morning, Jerome," she began, but Jerome ran around her side and straight into a tall black structure three little boys were evidently collaborating on. Their mouths filled with howls. He shot into the painting room, stopped at one of the tiny easels and seized the brushes. Before Mrs. Bradley, kneeling at eye-level with the children, had finished explaining that the new little boy hadn't

meant to spoil their building, it had been an accident, perhaps he would like to help them build—there was a high-pitched call from the painting room assistant. Rosemary ran in, thinking fast.

"Perhaps Jerome could work off some of this energy outside?" she said brightly to Mrs. Bradley, as she unhooked his fingers from the paint cans he had been throwing. The director nodded vigorously and went on mopping up the loud, color-dripping little victims. Before Rosemary could catch him, Jerome ran into the yard and tore a tricycle from someone and was riding in fast, wild circles, knocking over everything, child or toy, in his path. She blocked him at last and was holding him against her, trying to think what to do next, when Mrs. Bradley came out to her.

"Jerome, would you like to see our rabbits?" Jerome braced his face in Rosemary's lap and kicking backward like a horse, caught Mrs. Bradley in the stomach. Her face did not change as she signalled to another teacher. "Take Jerome in to see the rabbits," she said and the assistant, who was large and well-muscled for a woman, understood at once. Without a word she placed Jerome over her shoulder, and carried him away. Rosemary felt herself turning red. Mrs. Bradley sat down beside her and her face, too, was dark as though she had been wantonly insulted.

"You have not been frank with me," she began. "Your son is seriously disturbed. This is a school—not a dumping ground for psychiatric cases. You have not considered the other children!"

No, I damn well have not considered the other children, thought Rosemary. I consider Jerome, that's my job. Her throat was filling with anger. She made herself say, "His pediatrician suggested it. He needs help so much." She swallowed. "The waiting list at the Child Behavior Center is quite long. Time keeps passing. He needs help so much. Please give him a chance to settle down." She hunted through her bag for a Kleenex. "Please," she said in a low voice and blew her nose.

"I will call you a taxi," Mrs. Bradley said as she stood up. There were cries and the sound of blows coming from the building. Both women walked faster. The wind had disarranged Mrs. Bradley's efficient brown hair. "Altogether out of the question that he stay here. The Child Behavior Center is of course the solution. Meanwhile . . ." Her voice came to a stop. Mrs. Bradley was used to giving positive advice. "Meanwhile we cannot help you. I cannot endanger the other children."

The other children. Rosemary looked at them, clustered in the sandbox, swinging their clear colors by on the wheel toys. If she touched one of those bright faces it would be as warm as a rose under her hand. Nothing to it, she thought, and her mouth twisted. It would be common, coarse, just a reflex action to love children like those. They walked on. She had the absurd feeling that at any minute Mrs. Bradley would reach over and slice the buttons off her coat. Drummed out, out of the sight of healthy, normal children. Her fingers were cold and slipped against each other as she zippered Jerome in his jacket. For once he stood quietly. He even leaned a little against her. He finds all these children frightening, she thought. It was hard to know, but it seemed as though he was actually watching the other children. Suddenly he grabbed Rosemary's hand with a painful clinch. Would the taxi never come! Jerome held onto her hand tighter and tighter. I will not notice, I will not, she told herself. Her forehead felt wet and cold, too, and her arms ached, almost audibly, as though again under the weight of that quiet, white baby—Mrs. Bradley looked around the door and she was glad she could say, quite unnecessarily, "We're sorry to impose on you further, Mrs. Bradley, but the taxi hasn't come yet."

The taxi carried them home through streets now wide open to wind and the moving edges of shadows; the shifting mist was leaving and light hung from the trees like yellow leaves. There was no protection now, she was as exposed as he was. She rushed to the phone, Jerome still pinned to her side.

"Clyde, Clyde—they kicked us out!" Her lips thickened with tears that ran, unnoticed, down on the top of Jerome's stubby head. He was by now shuddering and heaving in a major tantrum, but Rosemary only held him closer.

"Honey, it was a long shot. We didn't really think we'd get away with it. Of course they don't want him!"

"They don't want us, they threw us right out!" One unit again, she and Jerome, one flawed unit. "They don't want us!" Rosemary hangs up the phone and rocks her struggling son back and forth. There are no barriers, no boundaries at all between them, and her wet face is glowing. A quivering lover is taking the caretaker's place, a lover who will awake in the night, broken by the passing of time.

PETER MEINKE

ELEGY FOR A DIVER

for R. W.

Jackknife swan-dive gainer twist
high off the board you'd pierce the sky
& split the apple of the devil sun
& spit in the sun's fierce eye.
When you were young you never missed,
archer-diver who flew too high
so everything later became undone.

Later everything burned to ash
wings too close to the sun broke down
Jackknife swan-dive gainer twist
can't be done on the ground
and nothing in your diver's past
had warned you that a diver drowns
when nothing replaces what is missed.

Everything beautiful falls away
jackknife swan-dive gainer twist
muscles drop and skin turns coarse
even skin the sun has kissed.
You drank the sun down every day
until the sun had ceased to exist
and only the drink had any force.

Only the drink had any force
archer-diver who flew too high
when you were young you never missed
& spit in the sun's fierce eye.
Later everything burned to ash:
everything beautiful falls away
even skin the sun has kissed
jackknife swan-dive gainer & twist

II

and now I see your bones in dreams
turning & twisting below our feet
fingerbones bending out like wings
as once again your body sings
swan-diving slowly through the stone
that sparks your skull and shoulder-bones
layer by layer and over and over
you flash through limestone sand & lava
feet together and backbone arched
like an arrow aimed at the devil's heart
the dead are watching your perfect dive
clicking their fingers as if alive
high off the board & the hell with the chances
once again your body dances
anything done well shines forever
only polished by death's dark weather
diver   diver   diving still
now & forever I praise your skill.

EVERYTHING WE DO

Everything we do is for our first loves
whom we have lost irrevocably
who have married insurance salesmen
and moved to Topeka
and never think of us at all.

We fly planes & design buildings
and write poems
that all say Sally I love you
I'll never love anyone else
Why didn't you know I was going to be a poet?

The walks to school, the kisses in the snow
gather, as we dream backwards, sweetness with age:
our legs are young again, our voices
strong and happy, we're not afraid.
We don't know enough to be afraid.

And now
we hold hopelessly the hope
that some day
she may fly in our plane
see our building   read our poem
and that night, deep in her dream,
Sally, far in darkness, in Topeka,
with the salesman lying beside her,
will cry out
our unfamiliar name.

AMON LINER

WITHIN THE INTERVAL

some write in a secluded place,
loud with flowers and water,
some write where lovers meet,
in cafes and in bed,
and some write from the place where I am
at the end of the world,

from which the sound depends,
as a grey-green bell
size of a child's head,
invisible.   In the air
of nonchalance,
the sound closes down
upon me, where I am,
at the end of the world,

where flowers grow,
grey as steel, brown as steel,
blue as steel, orange as steel,
vibrating in dirges and jingles
like any colors.   In the air
of surprise, sounds fade away
until only neutral tones
break my ears and I grow blind,
where I am, at the end of the world—

if there is such a place,
where grown knives circle in the air
and blood twists in huge, free-standing
columns, and eyes glitter
at every point.   In the air
of desolation, swinging
in the grey-green air, the child's head hollow
rings bell-like the sound
backward to shatter the clocks
I was when I was somewhere else, than here,
at the end of the world—

as if there were never any other place to go,
and no other age to make the journey.
It is a kind of a comfort
to write at the end of the world,
a place where all the nuances of grey
have their Just harmony,
and the blood collapses into the concrete,
and the knives rust on the counter,
and the eyes fade into light,
as the bell rings because the bell rings
whatever the hour and even if no hour
is this place, where I am, at the end of the world.

SLOW: CATTLE CROSSING

Another rambling MS
        a musicale of grumbling—
        At this age—ridiculous!
    I should be composing
            fruitfully
                skeins of formal spiels
        to advance the cause of maturity
                and perhaps gain golden trophies . . .

Up a blank wall,
        nailed with the nail of blandness,
        right through the eyeball,
            what can I see
            except what I am,
                which is where I am,
            which is noplace to even spend the night.

Where I am
        is what I am
            many intersections down which every road
    I've taken and it made no difference, all
            led to the same silence,
            the same blank-faced white-face
                mooning over the rail
                    beside the faded
                        roadsign.

ELIZABETH OAKES

A GIRL IS DEAD—13 FRAMES

The pavement
cools.
     A man
is walking
and sees the silhouette
of breasts and neck
on a shade.

Stretching,
she rubs on lotion
after a shower.

He sees
cool
water drops
on her
body.

The sheets
crackle, smell
of antiseptic.

She wakes
up as his hands
gouge her neck
and thinks
that she will wake
up.

Caught, she
wants to flirt—
but her eyes
cloud,
her hands
are not her own.

The last
vision
reflects
on the chenille.

He snatches
the breath
as it comes
out
of her mouth,
carries it cupped
in his hands.

He wears
the stigmata
of ordinary men—
his fingernails
peel
in layers,

his newspapers
lie crumpled
at his feet.

The maid
finds
an object
shaped like
a girl.

Strangers shake
their heads
on another
hot day.

HARRY MARTIN

REBECCA BROWN

FLINT KNIFE

The ruins of the pyramid stir
But make no answer to the water's tiny cry.
The Indian boy waves a fragment of lightning

I found thrust deep in the rocks
Among tombs broken by the sea and forest
With shards of idols wetly exposed,
Divine hands and thighs, and sometimes
With luck, the furious head of a snake,
Potsherds still painted with figures
Of suns and vermillion birds.

Laughing the boy plunges the flint blade
Into warriors and jaguars, unaware
Of the fury of burning planets locked
In its umber layers, ten million years'
Sediment, shifting continents and hurricanes,
Quartz carried from far plateaus
And hammered for an immolation
Or launching holy wars. His people believe

These flint points are fingers of ancient thunder.
Above him his fathers' temple rises silently
And walks down the hill to the water.

THE BROKEN IDOL

Burning the wilderness begins in winter
To plant maize before the rains. Beyond the river
Thunder prowls the scorched hills.

The boy Emiliano gave me the image
A tiny bird of stone and broken wings
Salvaged from a field of flaming pyramids.

I've found nothing with Emiliano
But mounds lost among charred streets
A cave of splintered pottery and swallows
Dark visions shriveling in ashes.

A family of toucans silently
Ponders the blackness of former trees
The sufferings of monkeys and crickets
And the smoking roots of a warrior's cry.

The squall will ride these cracked roads,
Far trees unfold in the rolling wind.
We gather the loose hours wildly

And barely reach the cave again
Before the rains break. Beyond the river
Thunder puts on green feathers.

SCORPIONS

In a desert that a dry wind
weaves out of broken bricks
and shards of plaster;
scorpions spiral, the
females swoon
but rise to eat the males.
Moving like tanks
over crumbs of rust
scorpions search for grubs,
white or yellow, to hoist away
and kill with their upturned tails.
Rattling their claws
over broken bottles
Holding fragments of stagnant dew
or rain, scorpions descend
to the cellar
open pitted to the sun.
Like armored horses they rattle
between broken flag stones;
flattening tin can down
when the stones are moved.

VOODOO

the dancers attempt shaking
jets from their hair
but
    the jets bomb sound
    through their soles.
from stretching hours
dark tales spin
legends stalking like
black sheathed girls with knives.

WILLIAM HARMON

from WILLIAM TECUMSEH SHERMAN —

Scorched coffee burns the morning tongue, blisters
The ridged roof of the mouth, waked in the oldest
    soldier's skull
    & bridge of his nose quickens to the burning of a
    hundred-year-old fence-post made of cedar;
Lice seem infinite anywhere there is hair on the body,
The oldest soldier's got the oldest shoes, kicks dew
    off the weeds in the breakfast line.

Tokens arranged in significant rows
                                          lexis, syntaxis
Scale: pawns: calculus: deliberate inventions in
    matrix, form begetting forms,
But not rocks in a stream, nor words in the air,
Not the cast of unanswerable stars in their great
    irregular night, & not the Army of the West arrayed,
    laid out more or less, for its celebrated expedition,
    ragged, across Georgia
Sky stony with smoke,
    smoke & shadows of smoke;
Dew dries from the weeds,
                        moisture rises from the drum heads.

Abundant & busy, positive
    as the succeeding generations of white maggots
The night of stars is skiing into its kiln,
Not a bee-line, nor as the crow, but crane foot, via the
    ecliptic, a great circle,
                                    evaporating.

Nor still nor steady
                            the sky moves
& the eyes move
                        with it,
Inhaling as it exhales, inhaling what it breathes out.

In the first light, then, widening upward over Stone
    Mountain, to the north,
Clouds come out of obscurity, emerge as a clearing
    fugue of fogs out of twilight lack of definition
& there take edge,
One whetted grey edge against the other, whiter grey
    edge
Of the sky,
                stone, the hide of the dried drum head;
Westward, the clouds as old shoes
    show mildew-colored half-light at the welt, grooves
    worn & polished
By the tough strings in the saddle-shaped tongue.

Toward Stone Mountain, then, the eyes, Major-
    General Sherman's eyes, move,
Following, in train, as the sky moves in itself, a sea
    of sorts,
Moves here & there & here again, once & once more,
Moves with leaves as a tree might, in the light &
    shadow of smoke, with the sun appearing, the sun
    showing through the smoke,
& the blood moves, & the lungs move in their housing.

ROGER WEINGARTEN

Any moment now he expects a thousand friends;
the stable he's tied to is a farm. In seconds
he will be tits to forty piglets, hive
to many drones, tired centaur, unwilling
Trojan Horse, phone booth about to be
stuffed, belly, sausage, steam room, stop.

The blue horse gallops across the stage
in agony, melting before an audience
of ice cubes. This is not the era
of his social success.

GREG KUZMA

On this truce of land and water
I have not made peace
but tramp loaded with ammo
almost sunk like the logs I trip on.
I think once of going under,
making dark thick bubbles
in the blue glass, found years
later and sealed in helium,
labeled "The Hunter".
I trudge.
The shore shifts,
acquires the mystery of girls'
legs in the drape of a dress.
In the confused tatters of bushes
the birds flutter with passion.
The cries of the ducks are close,
and there is the silence of crows.
I am covered by burrs,
my boots are barges,
my body a writhing cargo.
Yet I willed this.

From my car window weeks before
I passed the swamp
and told myself
here you will penetrate something,
an aggressor without audience,
meet nature head on,
battle her excess,
and find a pond beaded with ducks.

EMILIE GLEN

People of the living room
        Here to socialize
    Sit around in plexiglass
        So separate
They view one another
        Through smoked mirrors
The cat romping round the circle
    Where everyone sits as in corners
Is reached out to
        Petted
Not so much as the touching of fingertips
    Their words are streamers
        Mostly grey
    Shooting past each other
As the cat purrs to their pets
    They ghost come
        Ghost go
    Dipping fingers
Into the warm fur of the cat
    Later try to recall faces
        In the circle of corners
    Remember the feel of fur

GARY GILDNER

Standing at my window taking another smoke,
I see the man next door go down and stroke
alive his motorcycle, cool and firm
in tall blue riding boots. His wife's eye
disappears—but four blood brothers,
gripping eagles in their pockets, stand around
and see his moves are right. She doesn't squirm
this Indian bitch, she purrs—
she's got the classic lines, the itch
to go. No gap's been left too loose,
no spark to chance: the form is strict,
and four blood brothers keep it so—
they've got his knuckles for it, and his skin;
they've got the bones that wife across the way
who's counting beads and hiding
from the moon, can never know.

GERARD MALANGA

DAVID GALLER

10:viii:68

A young girl's immortality breaks
even in on my reality:
the contents of this poem are past
the past tense
the landscape absorbed by rain
drops as though toward the golden picture
frame through which I travel
expanding the limits of my eyesight,
the way Dante is unlimited, sometimes,
the transition might be easier
my desire is always desire to do the right thing
the countryside moving beside me
a young girl turns into a woman
walking through the tall weeds
in a wide open field
as I watch carrying a bowl of white fruit
the day of her first holy communion
You think one might share in this
experience the commitment
overcome by separation or the sky
light changing hands
in darkness then there is an historical perspective
to this world growing old without us "The back
side of the post card
reminds him of what he was like as a child"
was all a friend could tell me
in the new century
The lives continuing, but which
keeps the chain of events unbroken,
the correspondence preserved
under glass or filed and catalogued,
because the archives of the future are to be built
for research, for biographers.   Photographs:
It would be hard to remember
another way in which the space
is filled with your face
or two hands completing everything.

If the man's mother is not alone,
she will soon be, will want to be comforted;
so, he picks up the phone,
thumbing the news, but calls his wife instead.
Rather than say he will be late
and why, he asks if she has heard from their boy,
and murmurs he has a date
with an old friend.
                    "The riots could destroy . . ."
(is his girl home?) so claims the news.
The phone rings: his client saying *his* client
could use a broad and booze.
He makes the call; a voice is calm, compliant,
but she must be picked up, the fire
has spread to *that* part of town.
                                    His mother
calls: she has no desire
to see him or his wife; oh, what a bother
to bandage the boy's wounds . . . oh, *he's*
all right.
                    He calls his girl, who's been called by
his client. She wanted to please
him, she agreed to shack up with the guy. . .

He hangs up, starts to drink. His wife
calls: that same friend's come over, saying he's never
been so glad in his life—
The other line!—all right, *she* will come over,
the fire has spread.
                    Indeed. He hangs
up both.
                    His boy walks in, bandages bloody:
"Grandma's alone. . ." He bangs
the door in the kid's face: "*You* wait!"
                                    His ruddy
face sweats inside the shaft. He drinks.
Down in the lobby: *I might as well be dead,
nothing gets done. . . .*
                    He thinks
(thinking he hears the phone) of what Seneca said
to a friend once:
                    There having transpired
no loss, no gain, for years, he was glad to learn he
finally had acquired
more than enough provisions for his journey.

JONATHAN MORSE

Now you're that awkward dog that keeps the road dry
    in the rain,
you clumsy tube, or if you shelter a maggot word
it drops from you silently at the end. But kiss the rod:
your body lying there opens to love

and blossoms in a stare,
waiting under the rain you shift inside your decaying
    fur
adjusting to the road. You be the lid of the gravel,
you be the last dog crushed this aspect of the calendar,

now you're all right, jerking and popping. The
    different birds singing
into the improbable winter rain Aim-fire, Aim-fire,
    grasp
at their air perches. That is like nakedness heard
    through the wall
where you lie there under this but now you're the
    least of it,

and that's to be borne. Look, if we grasped our legs
    together
it would be the beginning of one kind of dream, but
    our night skins
would soften as the cold layers spread, that gel would
    lap off
in quiet threads, and we'd blend in your liquefying
    ears.

You have to be the dogskin draped over the gravel,
    the road animal.
There are covered sticks in the air, they stiffen our
    invisible breaths
and they penetrate you, but that's to be borne, now
    you're the last
and the birds catch air and sing in it, and live on the
    ice-sheathed wire.

EXPLANATION

Poe's hat stayed with him to the end,
that newmade Panama crushed and vomited on

and his stick, preserver of dignity, the Baltimore-
                                        broken
relic that he twitched

nervously up to his chest, and in his chest the unseen
                                        mechanical part
rotated like a clock and that too he kept,

the external reliable as his music, the figure
falling as if walking, breathing as if singing:

as if he were basing himself on his heart he fell
and that way he could reach the rhythm at last:

it was a gathering inward as he surrounded the gulf
of air, a covering the night with his body.

LYN LIFSHIN

SKIP BURNS

CHEEK

which humor goddess made my sister's face?

eyes grow huge, waiting to respond

cheeks are furrows of a meadow,
eroded and rebuilt by laughter.

lips bend while eyebrows lift,
tongue crawls out to touch her nose.

now she plays the stoic,
expressionless, composed through tickle's torture,

but the gaiety of her teeth and ears betray her.

LLOYD DAVIS

SUSPICION

Straining, he
hears a startled chair
pull together. Suddenly, all

over the house he seems to feel her
hair packing. Air
tastes out of place. He

listens for cigarette smoke in the
drain, for some damp
breath to moan out of pipes,

mounting his skull
with whose words were just there,
rubbing love to her belly.

Sponges gloat,
two glasses are shining like scars.
And the fear

bites against him
as he leans deeper into chrome, calls
wild thru sink coils after

her who may be
gone in moistness, already
sucked far under the house, skin

tumbling toward
better rivers. And who knows what watery
seducer riding

wet between her thighs, their gills
sleek, taunting him.
Black fin hair and wings smiling.

THE EUPHONIUM

depends on
        a pink coat hanger
                in the window of
                        not a pawn
                                but antique
shop
        an utterly
                youthless
                        silvered piece
                                of hollow brass
black
        in the crannies
                of its scars:
                        bell bent:
                                valve
stems
        like teeth
                lacking caps
                        (oh, mother
                                of pearl!)
oxidated
        into pantomime
                playing ((((boomb))))
                        to the long vacant
                                splints of a doll's
chair
        hung
                to the wall
                        by a Shaker
                                child

COLETTE INEZ

KELLY

Kelly's spongy mossland, pond and bog,
a noose around his curdling life
in Canada's tundra; tireless zinc, oil,
uranium, prospecting crones,
and the greedybitch "hit" that lures them on.

He waits: geiger-counting the million bucks
at night alone on his bunk.
Farina and beans, pepper and lard
stuffing his gut like a pregnant sow.

He dreams: baby-blue girls like watersnakes
to grip in the middle and cut their fangs,
on money's porch shouting his name,
Canada's mines to yield his claim,
the feast of fame in tomorrow's hunger.

Nights encased in snow, music scratching
   from Ottawa.
Meannesses recalled and dumped in the trash —
the pile of years. Niggling poor, how his
   father drooled
from a hyphenated mouth; lost deals, fiascos,
how he's telling it again to the purgatory gang

while mother's ironing prickly shirts for Satan's help
under the earth. A ring of flames around her feet
in shoddy mules. Her stoic eye collecting pain
like unpaid bills.

His fortieth summer: the tundra sags like a hammock
swinging mosquitoes, but the gold-piece
   sun hangs on,
a prosperous sky conjuring luck.
He hopes, and stays alive for a final "strike",
a gush of money to grease his life
now dry as crackers, poor as bone
in the spongy mossland, pond and bog.

CHRIS LAMSON-WHITE

Did you ever look into the eye of a king?
'Don't bother me about anything',
is the State he had aspired to.

One eye is on his army
for adventure and lure;
the other eye is on the topaz of his neighbor,
territories of women,
his picture everywhere the talisman.
All the while the tender milk-dew sky
is his announcement to himself.

When it's all over,
and he is bent with hiccups,
he must look down upon his straw feet,
wait upon his own door,
and hope for any befriending silhouette—

from his trees even the wind tangles
his hair with his tooth,
blinds his eyes with the grit of despair
and the howl in his throat is not heard.

ROBERT HILL

VERDI'S *REQUIEM* FOR A FADING TENOR

I wanted to speak and let him know
That somebody out there understood,
That *I* knew his voice and read
The too-wide tremolo as the lost
And terrified last age of the cords,
That I loved him for having
Once had a voice for "Ingemisco,"
Now gone, now uncomfortable for the audience,
As when my sympathetic past audiences
Cleared their throats and hacked for
My nervous phlegm and raspy notes.
I know him and wish better for him than
Polite applause one hour and a half after
A strange "Star-Spangled Banner" and
"The Lord's Prayer."

I wanted to speak, but I knew
It would be foolish and painful to recall
His wobbly "Dies Irae" and his
Late joining in with the chorus
To redeem something.

COLEMAN BARKS

TERRY STOKES

THE GIRL WITH BUCKTEETH & OTHER DREAMS

She was 12, an older woman,
skinny with buckteeth,
& a dirty black pony-tail, & she fell
every night
from a tree onto some rocks,
nearly,
but of course I caught her,
& gave her my I.D. bracelet.
It wasn't a bad dream at all.

Snake dreams followed.
Harmless, but clustered
the way snakes will
when they seek warmth, &
I would wake, never leaving
the bed, they were under it,
like the unused train set,
another snake-gift from my father,
not poison, just swirls in my nest.

& then, there were no dreams
to speak of,
the guillotine sliced my neck
like warm bread, & I never knew
who was holding the string,
a quiet trickle of blood, a thread,
rose easily on white flesh
in a soft room.

I do not remember the dreams which surrounded
the suicide attempt,
the search for fire escapes, naked,
the doctor thought that would keep me down,
bruised but nothing broken as usual.
I flap about for the girl with the buckteeth,
soon, her red crinolines will splash
like bird eggs dropping on the rocks
right outside my fragile home.

VENUS FLYTRAP

The dumb plant's mouth
closes thoughtfully on a pinch
of ground beef

and my cheap trick
on the green world

backfires. She opens up
early out of phase shows me
a blackened tongue and dies
consciously disappointed.

Hamburger won't do
she could decide
in some brainless, spineless
way within that one
electrical bud.

This was in graduate school
(when I roomed for a while
 with a guy in Biochemistry)
and I thought I was learning
something about the decisionmaking
process and digestion
or about desire and disillusionment.

When really all it was
was feeling that impulse
die out in her mouth.

LADY

By William Harmon

I

Lady O matrix an object a thing with holes in it

Lady doughnut torus standing naked in tears atop my bathroom scales, look

Lady here the soot goes in, hair comes out; here racket goes in, exit butts of wax; shades go in here, tears come out; here smells go in, snores and sneezes issue; here chow goes in, American English materializes, with kisses, little snowflakes on pane and petal

Lady now your convoluted navel is sealed like an abandoned salt mine, but once nourishment went in, excrement came out;

Lady here the money or love goes in, urine or kids come out, or the monthly blood; and in this place nothing is supposed to go in and what comes out comprises the subject matter for the arts and sciences of sanitation engineering

O Lady city country globe of a world or whirling galaxy! and

Lady anywhere at all on this rare matrix

Lady this complex net of flesh, see, a blade goes in and at the same door blood will come out, for

Lady you are an expensively upholstered ewe, dropped freshly wet from the noble Jacóbean cadences of David's psalms (the p is silent): we

Lady are His peeeeeeeople, theeee sheee-sheeeeeeeeeeeeeeeeeeeeeeeeeeeeeep

Lady lay your gates of thanksgiving down here next the still water for his name's sake, they

Lady are out to cut you for your virgin wool, butcher your body for mutton meat, reduce the edible remnants to glue and roughage for the Duke of Dogs (I saw him yesterday) and then

Lady render what's finally left of flesh and fat down to doctorates suitable for framing and deadstock tallow wax to materialize as the attentive candles at birthdays, weddings, anniversaries, and, finally, funerals

Lady all because your Will your dirty Id down there in the old dark cooks up new stews of lust, detailed recipes

Lady that chatter like a Teletype running open the catalogued imperatives of the litany of hiulcity *take-take-take-take-take* and

Lady hamhandedly the executing Ego of the ultimately impotent Will is subject only to the high-rise moby-readout of the super-tablets of the Law. *What*

Lady what on earth did you think you were

Lady some ever so slightly coarsened angel female and suffragan Virtue who by some cosmic miscue just happened to jump down off the great greensward felt of the Head Pool Hall of All

Lady to bounce with dainty bullseye accuracy across the barroom floor into the skunk-black bung-pit socket of the brazen one-holed cuspidor?

O lady you are nothing but a third-generation eel

Lady nothing

Lady nothing other than the earth's loudmouth *nouveau riche*

Lady wielding the razor of politics to barber the loins of your hogbristle biology but, hell

Lady it's still there, right down there in the old dark warm moist gulch or gully, a fungus-loving mother-oven spreading while you sleep

Lady it burns you but it won't itself go up in smoke

Lady for it's generating a brew of surprises for the spineless henpecked of this world of ours, but

Lady don't give in to it all the way, don't grow into one maw

Lady maw of muck eozoically going, going, coming, coming, in no different from out, up just the down of down and down up's up, heels over head, pedicure above lobotomy

Lady one thigh in the sinking Styx and

Lady one up to the hip in your own maw

O lady fix your face, spray your hair, lance your lobes for gold and rubies, glow in the dark, assume aluminum
siding if you must

Lady spend hours hiding your hide in modest stuffs, animal vegetable synthetic

Lady it'll be something else again tomorrow morning sure, right

Lady on the downright upright touch of six

Lady wait, wait and see.

II

Lady your story like your bottom won't hold water: now what

Lady in God's name really

Lady happened?

Lady you told us first that you *found* the egg laid by this "wild goose" that—or "who"—had been ravished in mid-
air and impregnated by some creature, presumably

Lady the notoriously active Father of the Gods in one of his zoological outfits

Lady he having previously made a pass at some earlier and evidently humanoid incarnation of said goose; and
then

Lady you turned right around and said that Hermes—it *was* Hermes, was it not?—threw the egg—is that right?
threw the egg

Lady between your queenly thighs as you were seated on a stool of sorts—

Lady let me get this straight—

Lady sitting on a stool of sorts with your legs did you say "apart"? Very well. And

Lady it was during the period of time that you were situated on this particular birth-stool *(sic)* the holy child
appeared, was somehow born? I beg your pardon

Lady so now, now you say the truth really is that you were indulging in a sun-bath clad in your let us say
birthday suit down by the river, whereupon

Lady a swan—is that correct? a swan?—this *swan* happened by and, in the course of events, the two of you

Lady you and this "large, web-footed, long-necked, gooselike bird," to wit

Lady swan: you and this alleged swan did then and there

Lady do

Lady the deed?

O lady you were forced, I see, I see, of course, and that makes all the difference in the world, oh absolutely

Lady indeed: the "swan" compelled you, forced you, made you

Lady carry out, perpetrate, commit this act which

Lady needless to say you would not otherwise have accomplished of your own free will and volition for love or
money; after which

Lady the swan hailed you "handmaiden," "seastar," and all the rest of it? Please

Lady hold your lamentations, contain yourself, hold your water if you would

Lady I mean to say, just let me point out it's too late now, the hand is dealt, ferocious internecine face-cards
tearing at each other with their teeth

Lady their looking-glass-image double rows of predatory teeth that have no upside-down; and furthermore

Lady I would be the first to admit that none of this *affaire* was your fault unalloyed, no, not a bit of it

Lady did anyone ever suggest the exclusive possibility of such spontaneous combustion of your royal uterus? Or
unassisted singlehanded procreation of a tribe of unexampled troublemakers?

Lady nobody ever heard of such a thing, so

Lady relax.

Lady now dwell for a moment if you would, please, upon this magically gifted swan's patently unusual, peculiar
anatomy, and

Lady try to tell the court just what it felt like to partake, to be

Lady in other words to be a member of the celebrated beast with two backs

Lady in conjunction

Lady with a bird. (O amicable cob!) Please

Lady overlook my most impolite outburst, if you will, and try to continue with your account, your description
of the physical sensations you could not have helped but experience while on the receiving end of this
transaction. Very well then

Lady failing that, perhaps you would be good enough to recount what, as the resultant aftermath of such traffic with such an exceptional creature,

Lady you surely felt along the lines of shall we say motherly delight when watching this egg (and

Lady we are all agreed on that one fact if nothing else whatever: there was

Lady an egg, though

Lady none may know for certain now what kind of egg it was, what size or shape or color, or how or why or when or where or whence it came to be,

Lady the egg did exist beyond the smeary touch of doubt or printer's ink in one of those unkind canards that are the staple by means of which the muckmakers of periodical literature and the cathode ray survive— God curse the Declaration of Indulgence!) yes

Lady yes: item: fact: the egg was there, there was the egg. And as you watched it hatch

Lady what did you feel? Did you melt or freeze? Ah: "Mixed emotions." Mixed indeed, beyond all question, yes, and

Lady now your hands and eyelids bear for all to see the tracery of that grim polygraph,

Lady they display the ratlines of the networked strain and suffering of that unique delivery, whatever shape it took

Lady along with its unlucky issue for every Tom, stock, and cranny of the human race from China to the moon, near which

Lady the constellation "Swan" is viewed each evening by dedicated members of the northern-hemisphere chapters of the cult

Lady a swan, but not, we know, just *any* swan

Lady this excellent and indispensable constellation—now listen carefully—this sidereal raree-show is—let me get this right—am I to understand

Lady that the constellation "Cygnus" shows, in outline, not the graceful indolent animal familiar in all our many public parks and individual estates, but O my dear

Lady displays instead *the bottom view of a swan in flight?* (Too much

Lady much much too much) and

Lady in this, well, superlatively unprepossessing prospect I take it there dwells one particular radical star, a white dwarf of the second magnitude or so, that represents, encapsulates, epiphanizes

Lady the root of all our evil?

Lady is that correct? And is that then the reason for the constellation's being also called "The Northern Cross"? Would you

Lady expect these highly educated gentlemen to believe for one single moment that—that—that

O lady how I hasten to subject my extravagant fancy to its customary discipline in order that I might resist the puissant temptation to denominate it

Lady a Cock and Bull story?

Lady this song and dance of yours? Now

Lady tell the truth: does not the clean clear voice of Blessed Ockham's Razor tell us all in no uncertain terms,

Lady does not, I say, in all humility, does not that loyal-bladed instrument on every bathroom shelf announce sans ambiguity that

Lady some simpler explanation surely must exist than this fantastic science-fiction tale of yours, this Mother Goose's fable you're attempting to palm off on us, this tissue of sheer undemythologized corruption, vice, lubricity, and sin? Why, why not

Lady a baboon? Divine rhinoceros? Or deified giraffe? Hows-about a horny kangaroo or emu from the continent "down under"? (That

Lady does not sound too altogether inappropriate.) Why not even the unspeakable parakeet that dangles in cute captivity of every tacky kitchen of the working class? Why, O Jesus, why not

Lady the char's repulsive budgie? Why not Donald Duck? Indeed, indeed, indeed

Lady what's to prevent or interdict your gleefully coupling with the very eagle screaming on the justly famous backside of each and every dollar bill in These United States? Why

Lady why not go right ahead and implicate, nay, put the finger on that innocent yet formidable emblem, symbol, and image of invincible imperial republican democracy, rampant and erect? (Forsooth

Lady there's something in his eager yellow eye, God knows, besides the budget.) No

Lady it won't wash. I have turned Krafft-Ebing upside-down and inside-out, I've ripped the guts from Kinsey and Associates and M. Girodias

Lady not to mention exotic monographs beyond your power to pronounce or comprehend

Lady and nowhere

Lady nowhere in all that thirty bulky tons of pornopsychiatric bibliography have I unearthed, discovered anything, of annotations, spices, *or* perversions, that can in any way compare to this

Lady your desperate last-ditch attempt at—what's it called nowadays?—*romantic irony*? Now

Lady the provenance of these four, or three, or two, or, okay

Lady if you prefer, just one unbelievably pernicious egg is no red herring

Lady no stupid quart of purloined berries, no horrors from the Pole of Hollywood

Lady no hunt for fictitious witches under every bed in this our District of the Discovering Dove, no

Lady no: the origin of evil, attached in some mysterious way to your power to bear, or bring into the world
by any agency whatever, and then to educate

Lady at least one daughter, if not two, your presence

Lady as the spring of evil is the question of the century, and

Lady I want to go on record here and now in public as believing with every fiber of my power to believe that

Lady your contumacious coyness is the first and at the same time the last word in disobedience! It is itself, I
might almost say, the radix—

O lady don't you cry now, don't cry, please, I didn't for one single minute intend, mean to rail against you *as
a person, personally,*

Lady please, here: help yourself to my hand-rolled handkerchief, forgive me

Lady (blow—good, good) look: my enemy is the enemy of us all, of you as well as of these august philosophers
assembled to examine your misfortune, ill-starred catastrophe, and

Lady now please don't cry, please, just think back, try to remember, if you will

Lady nil desperandum, nil, nil, nil, believe me, NIL, please believe me

Lady please, please

Lady—

III

Lady standing in tears amid my spacious bathroom

Lady twice-divorced mother of two strong sons, an Andy and an Ed

Lady two-fathered yet fatherless, now far and farther away

O lady in tears and nothing else

Lady among the immaculate maroon fixtures and furnishings, Klee's *Komödie* warping on the wall

Lady a corral of unemphatic grey figures, a great piece for my money,

Lady between the grinpaste and the Northern softness (s-o-f-t-n-e-s-s
                                                        N-o-r-t-h-e-r-n)

Lady what you are to me: one consonant and an *o*, three consonants and an *e*, two consonants, then nothing

Lady

O lady bawl no more please if you please

Lady that's enough for now

Lady they might hear, they can hear through the flocked walls

Lady your defenseless bosom has no buckler now, *kein Büstenhalter,* if you like, softness is Northern

Lady I do believe it really, really is. I'm sorry

Lady don't say I have no *scruple* (no one-third of a dram? no twenty grains? no twenty-fourth part of an
ounce?) nay

Lady as you have seen, the evidence is but abundant: my kitchen bitches under the weight, the gravity, the
gravidity

Lady of ten-dollar half-gallons, shelf on shelf

Lady it was "buckler" I said: *scutum*

Lady s-c-u-t-u-m: I was alluding to your underwear

Lady but that's all in your past

Lady moons gone now, way way back, a room removed

Lady the lighting in here is indirect

Lady fluorescent to turn your made-up lips purple

Lady the gleaming handle of the electric toothbrush is your friend, and the fat white sheepskin carpet, the
chummy robe of terry

Lady the shower curtain is on your side, it matches the drapes and they rhyme with your eyes, look

Lady the water in the jolly tank is in your corner, egging you on, cheering just for you, it jumps, look, at my

touch, thus, flinging pompoms of encouragement to the wind for you, behind you all the way, I said I
was sorry

Lady say: now listen, tell me this: What walks on one leg?

Lady dry, here, reel off a fathom or two of Northern tissue, and have some dental floss while you're in the
reeling-off mood (I often am)

Lady dry

Lady don't cry, there's no need to make a federal case out of—not the end of the world, dear, rest assured

Lady that if it were the end of the world, why you'd have every right to make a federal case out of it, and

Lady believe me, I'd be right there by your side every step of the way with veritable Mormon Tabernacle
Choirs of legal paper, long briefs, true bills, and papal bulls if need be

O lady don't spoil those pretty cheeks with tears, old ugly tears. Now

Lady I answered your riddle, didn't I? It is I, I said, goes four legs, two legs, three (diplomatically allowing a
certain latitude of riddler's license, I think, in the extension of the ordinary definition of "leg")

Lady so don't tell me some goddamned impromptu *monopod's* the answer, no

Lady no and no and no. I keep as you can easily see a dictionary handy just for days like today: Volume . . .
six. Well. What do you know?

Lady *monopode*, but that's not what you said, exactly, and besides it comes from Pliny—

Lady if you'd tell me what I had done

Lady if I just knew what it was I said that set you off like this, or had some hint of just what my Big Sin was,
why

Lady I'd do more than apologize or get down on my hands and knees to humbly beg your pardon

Lady I'd take the errant hand or tongue or whichever of my parts it might have been

Lady and cut it off: look

Lady stacks and stacks, five-packs of blades, the very keenest edge on earth, expressly designed and executed
by the long-established manufacturer to cut

Lady carve to the quick quick quick! Now

Lady look here a color tube with UHF, AFC, CBS, three tiers of speakers like a labor rally, tape deck
zriiiiiiiiiiiiiiiiibpdt!, the collected works of good old Rusty Warren

Lady and Nabokov doing *Lolita* at thirty-three and a third revolutions per minute (now that's Microgroove for
you), Hemingway's *Saturday Night at a Whorehouse in Montana*, hell

Lady *all* the classics, now

Lady there's no clear reason for your springing neap of tears

Lady least of all here in my papally appointed toilet, see

O lady see the little people of this world at peace: the bottles do not sob, they do not spill a single drop over
some imagined slight,

Lady unweeping the tubes sleep the sleep of the innocent, the air-bombs have no bone to pick with the world,
no axe to grind,

Lady see here, silent, ungriping, like a log, *ecce* the roll-ons with their neat round heads like a phalanx of white
pawns. Now

Lady just take it easy please: the jelly on your thighs is quivering

Lady that's right: sit.

Lady would you like me to lift the lid for you? And here

Lady pills, Babylonian piles of pills for every ailment known to mankind, placebos, panaceas, Galen's horde and
Paracelsus' treasury: cathartics

Lady and specifics for any fear you feel, everything from externally caused pimples and blemishes to the Second
Coming, pharmaceuticals

Lady bottled, boxed, in needles, vials, tubes and capsule-form (do

Lady lift the lid if)

Lady look: the tile itself is neatly laid from wall to wall for you, peruna pattern, see with what precision and
grace it meets here the edge of the tub bottom

Lady how very thin the line of mortar, nice, for

Lady it's your friend, and look: the wholesome oakum calking around the flange that grips the pipe here where
it goes into the floor belongs to you

Lady like all these nostrums, powders, tonics, and elixirs here: pills to sleep and pills to not, pills to make you
fat or trim

Lady and these precious jewels from my own babied herb garden just beyond the kitchen dooryard, these will stop both diarrhea and constipation: see

Lady they take your present status, no matter what, bar none, and gently, gently return you in a trice to your normal

Lady and healthy regularity. And here is a device I earnestly hope you never feel the need of, but should it happen that you do feel the need, well,

Lady here it shall always be for you in its modest unmarked box of solemn black, disagreeable in the end, as I am only too well aware

Lady but essentially and deep down in its heart of hearts a thing of virtue.

Lady behold this larder stuffed to the gunwales, full to overflowing, a fountain and unqualified cornucopia of linen

Lady in every race, creed, and color, all for your delight

Lady and here a lazy susan of assorted periodicals (*SP Esquire Woman's Home Companion Cornhill Field & Stream Sunshine & Health Hot Rod* and the house organ of Alcoholics Anonymous, *The Grapevine*) and

Lady many many books, a little night music, *Schmutzliteratur,* see

Lady a thousand volumes of pornography: pornography, pornography, pornography, the *Purgatorio,* and more pornography, pornography, *O,* pornography, (*The Cardinal's Mistress,* by Mussolini, is not pornography, oddly enough), more pornography

Lady this is a collector's item *sui generis:* pornography, you're quite right there, the pictures tell you that, but observe: it's *Chinese Communist* pornography

Lady you must admit you won't see things like that in just any poet's head.

Lady see: pornography, pornography, pornography *par excellence et de rigueur,* pornographypornographypornography Gray's *Anatomy,* por—but no

Lady this is Calvin's *Institutes,* my golden book: no scruples?

Lady I am in command of resources, raw and human alike, beyond the meagre scope of your arithmetic to tally

Lady just how many natural numbers do you think you have? *The Pilgrim's Progress* porpopornopornoporno the *Odyssey* pornporn Poe (poor Poe) popopopopopopopopo ppppppppppppppppppp

Lady

Lady ah! now, there

O lady that's so much better: a smile, a smile, a small small smile

Lady the minimum smile in all our universe I realize, of course, but yes, no doubt about it

Lady a smile. Now

Lady look here: a seahorse taming Neptune for a change, here Leda giving the Zeus the business (you blush), here Jesus nails the crucifixioners, here blacks practice prejudice with more than just a vengeance, here Edgar Guest

Lady ridiculing critics, here policemen undergoing a third degree, and

Lady here is skill at last controlling folly, and well

Lady that's what you might call metapornography, but it will do to swell a progress, start a scene or two, if you know I mean.

Lady ha! now "name your poison": lo: a steamer trunk of booze: bourbon, brandy of the peach, the pear, the plum, the apricot, the pomegranate, a pint of fireroom raisinjack from my old destroyer, and here

Lady my M14, hold it in your hand, it can deal out twenty rounds, look

Lady set like *this* on automatic, this way, here, will fire all

Lady all twenty rounds in a matter of seconds . . . . Wow

Lady and here's a samurai baron's auto-destruct mechanism, this is a fragmentation grenade

Lady of course it works, it's no communion wafer, get your pretty little teeth

Lady off that goddamned pin

Lady and by the way

Lady excuse me, could I get there a second? Thanks

Lady didn't I tell you? *Softness is Northern,* well

Lady there's proof for you, right there, and here

Lady proof positive (if any more were needed)

Lady a 12C shoebox filled to the very brim with rabbits' feet, yours to keep, all of them your special buddies, friends to bring luck to you and you alone

Lady and these hopalong horeshoes nailed up around the room: all yours

Lady and these quatrefoil clovers, beautifully laminated in amber, just for you

Lady for you this lucky penny, the first I ever made *EGOD*

Lady here a bunch of mistletoe blessed by the Druid pontifeximus, ah
Lady ah there
Lady there's the laugh I knew was left in you, I knew you had it in you, it isn't so terrible then
Lady is it now? Yes, dear: affirmative: please do, lift the lid, get rid of it, all moods and tenses of it
Lady you know I was ill once myself with mononucleosis and sat so with simultaneous diarrhea and nosebleed, cursing
Lady the day that I was ever born and all my parents' parents' parents back to Eden
Lady but like you I learned to laugh, to laugh it off, to laugh it up, that's it, that's the *Way*
Lady there, laugh, as I did, amid my woes and troubles and trials and tribulations, laugh and be absolutely happy and carefree
Lady
O lady seated there in joy here in my spacious bath.

IV

Lady you've been (occasionally I think here in the dark) the novelist's monopoly too long
Lady because it just may be that the roots of modern feminism (if that's not a contradiction in terms) are woven, raddled together with the roots of fiction *(Oroonoko)*
Lady the drama an older form, so the sexes run half and half (discounting of course the conventions of the all-male Elizabethan theatre: Cordelia with a dick—phenomenology can go too far!), but
Lady in poetry, most old, the senior service, the Word in the beginning, where it really matters, women don't figure at all except as domesticated animals or dim-perceived influences
Lady something like prudence or breathing or gravity, memory a mother, muses succubae (as I well know), yes
Lady but precisely because it is there it is without importance,
Lady as in Ovid where the art of love is simply a pastime about on a par with playing poker
Lady worth a little work, demanding a mind, fraught with duplicity and politics and even hazard if you go too far, to be sure, but
Lady fundamentally a trifle. Subsequent *Frauendienst*
Lady the cult of courtly sublimated masturbation was the hermetic antithesis, as boring in the end as Ovid gets to be
Lady the urging of the reproductive atoms vaporized to a mist of systematic fiction, the angular cathedrals thrown groined up on the altar in the lap of Our Lady of Perpetual Erection, a graph of the powers of three ascending
Lady videlicet acute Panovsky on the *Summa Theologica:* "A veritable orgy both of logic and Trinitanian symbolism"
Lady and remember "the upward springing motion of the broken arch" cast of a thousand Babels shot upward
Lady an orgy, the particles of soul propelled through space like Salisbury's bonehead arrow, wilting in declension
Lady then darkened in Shakespeare, tried three times by Milton, hoist in Gulliver's petard (M-26 fragmentation fart, just pull the pin and lob, love)
Lady finally displayed anatomized across the polyphonic night
Lady of Richardson's million terms, ever-dodging ambiguities, divisions halved and coupled, ironies, ratlines running from any one star in the firmament to any other
Lady simple, multiple, complex variable constellations, your swan my cross, ultimate glyph, zoötomy of lowest lust and purest saintliness
Lady in *Clarissa,* synthesis and manifesto: *The proper study of mankind is woman* (I know this doesn't interest you at all
Lady but bear with it: it's a queer wheel that won't roll) and *The study of Our Lady lays bare,* says Henry the Ninth, *lays bare the whole subject of sex*
Lady while ("mortally afraid of Madams") laying nothing really bare from one end of his days as the dynastic original Conservative Christian Anarchist to the other
Lady no matter what Empson might say about one end of a stick having to be the beginning
Lady he (Henry) did roll out the rug for Frazer and Graves and Lawrence to stand on
Lady while warming their modest buttocks near the existential fireplace *(focus),* and
Lady there you have it, there you are: Goddess of Anthropology, O bitch-tail of the wagging northern star
Lady for every magnet pin, bottommost nadir of the easy polished bannister of generality
Lady root of roots, but sparkling zenith too, and between the two
Lady doomed, as the first best Huxley observed a hundred years ago, doomed to the weight of motherhood,

potential if not kinetic in explicit childbirth, so that

Lady the effort to balance the womb's weight by idolization only serves, as is the case with so many gallant attempts at balancing, to double the tonnage.

Lady queen of any given hive or heaven, daughter and star of every sea, heiled by automatic arms

Lady and kneecaps and lips programmed like computers

Lady you also cook and sweep and wax and raise kids, work never done and love your whole existence, which

Lady alongside the burst shards of the male's way of living does have, at both extremes, a satisfying wholeness to it (what that mad molecule McLuhan maintained was "homogenization") and should, conceivably, *conceivably*

Lady vouchsafe to you a more trustworthy foolproof vision of the truth of things, not so? Hey

Lady not so?

V

Lady some days

Lady are what I call Blake days, when I leap out of my Blake

Lady at Blake o'Blake in the splendid Blake

Lady brush my Blakes and go forth polished

Lady like the Heavenly Host exploding in hydrogen hosannahs O soprano alto tenor bass in one enormous operatic symphony for the Sun of Everlasting Mercy

Lady a kind of diamond of perfected intellectual beauty manifest in music

Lady Handel for example objectified in crystals of External Reality

Lady minute particulars in the City of the Lake of Salt beyond the river, then

Lady I drive along the six-lane *via* in my tuned up physical body of fate, points and plugs never missing a trick, sharper than a barber, and

Lady even stuff like rain and garbage looks okay, sunshine a visible essence of gold and color of gold through mist,

Lady white boots discarded by a discontinued majorette among lovely banana fells and the song of ugly gulls a *Gloria*.

Lady bunky

O lady lying on your starboard side, an evergreen figure in a landscape of veteran percale

Lady supporting the right side of your rather heavy skull with your right hand falling asleep at the wrist

Lady reading *An Island in the Moon* for me, our golden book with no dark side, ideal

Lady with a three-flush of albino leopards under juniper the picture on the label of a bottle of economical Belgian gin

Lady or one showing a shot of *Victoria Regina et Imperatrix* dewlappy just eactly like Mayor "Dick" Daley of Chicago (that tottering town) but

Lady let us forget bad things today and concentrate exclusively on our home happiness, for some number of seconds, here and now, for

O lady all days are not Blake days: some days are just hogs, hogs, long tons of pure boar skinned out, stretched

Lady from far east to far west, hiding the sky, rackstorm obscuring the stars, then

Lady I come to in my pockmarked george, my johnquincy aching, andys all bleary with three separate layers of pistachio-colored williams of johnjames, I

Lady don my ratty zack and roll like a cueball on its way to scratching in the corner pocket down to the millard with its watt on a string, where

Lady I, green as something the dog puked up (or, if that particular figure is as disagreeable as you seem to think, green as something the dog didn't puke up) sit my unlovely franklin down on the below-wow-zero bachelor jim

Lady and take a great roaring railsplitter honest abe, succinct toadstools under mushroom cumulus, afterwards tidying my andy with foolscap ulysses in a fourfold rutherford (northern softness, *laus Botulo*)

Lady then slip a new stainless jimmy into my chet and therewith reap a harvest of the miserable congregated little grovers from off my horny field of ben, pitiful, amen, then

Lady brush my chartreuse bills with 2 cc's of bearmoose squeezed onto the dying williams of my antediluvian woodrow

Lady palm on a daub of warren to keep my cal from smelling up the Otis coffin of the elevator shoe I go up to my office in, force my jowly herbs into artificial wingtip franks

Lady knot my harry s with a four-in-paw (the only thing I ever learned in school) and sidewinding skid in my

slipping used ike down to the jack where I take my second lyndon of the morning, et cetera, you don't
    want to hear all this

Lady

O lady my presidio, let us forget, let us forget

Lady beneath whose awful hand I hold dominion over this and that, a life of trifles with sometimes concentric
    halos glowing like emphatic factorials (!) in a dream of Cartesian space

Lady time gone

Lady let us forget.

Lady at last

Lady now the index of sincerity is style, presumably

Lady but all that really matters and all I care about is subject matter

Lady subject matter pure and subject matter simple, and I don't care one jot or give a single fig

Lady about the treatment, paper on the wall of the matrix, not a bit.

Lady in our about-to-become-jetsam counterfeit of dialogue, allusions are too excremental, don't you think?
    Too derivative,

Lady piecemeal, dead, unmistakable *Niederschlag,* that is, sediment

Lady precipitate

Lady anonymous flotsam, fallout of something once alive and vital

Lady as all our food was once, with

Lady the possible exception of salt, and I like salt, I am very fond of salt, I love salt

Lady so much so that I've often thought of taking the pickup down to the feed-and-seed store

Lady to buy for myself one of those big lemon-yellow salt-blocks on a post, bull's popsicle. And I hasten to add
    cow's too

Lady Laconia

Lady love allow me my indulgence of going out in an absolute blaze of bunk

Lady *(tempus tacendi . . . muβ man schweigen* etc.) there surely must be plenty of time for silence in the tomb

Lady still and all, a dime's worth of corn meal goes a long, long way

Lady have patience (this nosegay of transcendental meditation makes Coleridge sound like Eisenhower, but
    then who among the generals that decked Troy was an eloquent ruler?)

Lady take my pocket and the handkerchief within and all the paper scraps, for

Lady I talk all the time, almost always, almost every day, because I am convinced that rational discourse among
    men of good will

Lady will usher us into the chamber of truth

Lady the throne room.

Lady

O lady gone, now only total shadow (not darkness, not absence, not loss) only total shadow

Lady this room is the darkest room when rooms are dark, and quiestest when it wants to be

Lady with the water clock stopped, nothing left to tick or glow in the dark, only total shadow of the room—

O lady lady Zoo of me I beat myself to pieces against the bars, am strained through the sawteeth of the mesh

Lady I land again and again and again at the polluted bottom of impossibly broad moats that know my
    strength and exceed it by an agonizing inch

Lady I was not born for these impolite latitudes, I do not eat right in captivity, the kids deposit candied
    handprints on the glass to keep me from forgetting them too soon

Lady I shall not play my customary games in plain sight, nor mate with any random dam they drag in (poor
    things, poor things)

Lady the touring journalists and bra ad fans shall not snap my balls with cameras, I make impassioned grabs for
    their Japanese straps and gadget bags and

Lady wind up chained up yodelling my umlauts of despair in a cramped wind tunnel unheated and unclean

Lady and only sleep when shot full of heavy doses of dull numbing drugs and even then

Lady my gills tremble for that's not proper sleep, the copulation of the chemicals with the open lesions in my
    soul breeds monsters

Lady and I dream

Lady Luray, Lubyanka, Wormwood Scrubs, Poulo Condore the prison island, me Mudd

Lady eventually awake however and however and however.

VI

Lady as now the golden-crownèd sun surrenders the field at the day's edge

Lady with a fading spectrum of rainbow-colored lances at the dissipating margin of the great light
Lady the rose and ivory tones come and go in your face around the blue-green-gold casualty center of your eyes when
Lady every morning a hundred-percent virgin despite no matter how prolonged an indulgence in your thermometer-bursting debauchery the night before
Lady you quite subdue the monster unicorn. He
Lady is hardly the prettily curried miniature spaniel pet of romance tapestries or the one-horned pony painted cowboy white, no
Lady he is altogether horrible and huge, as the senior Pliny pictured him, Clydesdale-trunked, stag-faced, elephant-heeled, boar-tailed
Lady with a voice that roars along at a steady thirty Hertz, no more, no less
Lady the neck short and thick, plus flat nose, grey bloodlaced eyes that can't see much, and deaf hair-clogged ears
Lady and the horn is six feet long, at least, and all solid black
Lady with nicks and dents as ugly trophies of encounters with rhinoceros burglars who would usurp his legend or
Lady the blue or white sea-Dicks who attempt infringements on his ancient patent.
Lady the infallible efficacy of your iron virginity in putting him to sleep is admirable, and
Lady I come with nets and hypodermic darts to put a cap on his captivity, so
Lady the Company for which we toil can cross him with a trembling jenny and produce a race of wheelhorses potenter than any mule on earth, and
Lady breed him to herds of scream-prone lady zebras to give rise to carnival attractions of unprecedented drawing power
Lady panphotogenic stars of supermarket parkinglot loudspeaker monsteramas
Lady and scare the kids to death. They love it.
Lady and make possible our newest zootheogony as when
Lady you pause to ponder, reading a treatise on the religions of Egypt, upon being reminded
Lady that the father of the gods was named *Nut*
Lady who got a modest wooden start in life no doubt as some local dog-skulled *Polluto*
Lady about a quarter's worth of otherwise no-good lumber come scorched from a blitz-split oak
Lady something about the size of one of your shoeboxes put up on a shelf
Lady and tossed after-supper sops of sacerdotal fat and gristle nobody in his right mind would want to eat anyway
Lady and maybe on May Day every other leap year given a virgin of fifty so unappealing she might as well be sacrificed to him. Thus
Lady the *Nut-Pluto-Plutus* syndrome: a lot of laughs, ample wallet-grave holding both the god of wealth and the god of death (days and years
Lady die and rise again, planting vain parabolic hopes in the minds of men) wealth and death married in a plural melody
Lady not unlike the USA today
Lady 200 million people with a GNP zooming towards a trillion annual clams
Lady and yet not even enough wit to stop up a newborn gnat with dysentery. Not a culture
Lady nor (in Spengler's terms) a civilization, but just a *civ*.

Imagine

Lady praying O Pluto 1930 outermost planet and hoar-star presiding over the Depression
Lady an ugly runted wandering chunk of clinkerage from the bottom of the sun's furnace
Lady an England of a planet, a model hell where the off season goes on all year long and the year
Lady goes on for ninety thousand winter nights, influencing earth
Lady in the same decade of Depression manifest as Disney's Mickey's pup in that unlovely catalogue of animal gods: more doggy than Goofy the human hound gate-toothed and doomed in business suits and hillbilly hats over cliffs down wells
Lady this Pluto is a virgin gelding of limp tail, flat absolute feet, bad breath, a rug-red diving-board tongue and eyes like hockey pucks; yes
Lady future archeologists will decipher our time-tapes and conclude in chorus
Lady that "M'cKeymou seems to have been a three-fingered holy rodent, hermaphrodite-throated, attended by an apparently barren female, two fatherless (orphaned? bastard?) nephews (*Fert* and *Mort*), and a

bad-tempered sea-going duck, along with (according to the *Codex Arminii*) a saffron-colored retarded mutt named *Budda* or *Blud(o)*—

Lady sing: O God of Death please bless the German poet Grass, that he resurrected Hitler's *Prinz* as a new *Pluto*

Lady sing: and bless as well in the plenitude of your benevolence our Central Intelligence Agency, that it revived the World War II *Unternehmen* name Operation PLUTO to be the code word applied to the 1961 amendment to the Monroe Doctrine enacted down near the Bay of Pigs; for now

Lady the sleeping dog lies on the bottom, as unmarked fighters from the *Essex* circle like jays whose nest has been upset, but

Lady he will rise again from the sea another miracle of April when

Lady soot of star falls and the sundial-index thorns appear along the bones of the apple-colored rose

Lady sprung in delight from the green ground under the skeleton of a unicorn becoming year by year more ivory

Lady how the rows of ribs branch out in a network of cobwebs, how

Lady the hollows of nostril and pelvis hold water, and how a gnomon shadow falls from the horn across the tickling leaves.

Lady let another language speak the grass-green light hailing from heaven through the jungle's ceiling, its double canopy

Lady hundreds of feet up, summer, winter, the same

Lady with birds of paradise uninterruptedly tomorrrowing

Lady among cherries and mint

Lady while rose-mouthed hell-birds bloody the petals pecking each other to mincemeat for the hot potpies that

Lady accompany the limericks and tambourines and practical jokes to the triple rainbow circus

Lady and cosmetic Easter emerges from made-up eggs in a smell of vinegar and resurrection

Lady it will burst forth in colors of rose and gold and ivory into the green leaf-spring and

Lady down the bending year.

A MAYPOP FROM MERTON

Illustrated by Mary Mintich

BY SYLVIA WILKINSON

I won't look up, I just won't. If he starts hollering at me, I'll just act like he's not even there. I know if the school bus doesn't get here soon, he'll make me cry just saying one ugly thing about the way I look. He always says the wrong thing; if it's not that I've got lipstick on my teeth, he'll ask me what that white thing sticking out the bottom of my skirt is and then I go around all day long feeling like I'm just thrown together. With my head down I can't help but cry, the tears just run out even when I don't feel like it and my face will be streaked like I got blood poisoning; it will, I've got that kind of skin. It's delicate and people tell me I should be proud of it but sometimes when I cry when I don't mean to, I mean when I just bend over and tears run out of my eyes, it can just be

embarrassing. But he has a way of picking on me and I let it bother me. I don't know why. I just do. I'd give anything in this world if I didn't let somebody like him bother me.

He is a full year older than me and I caught up with him in the seventh grade and he is still there. They let him go on to the ninth grade in Sunday School and I get stuck with him following me around and looking at me like I could ever care two cents for him. Giving me that valentine with his name in numbers thinking I didn't have enough sense to figure it out to be him . . . 13-5-18-20-15-14. I hadn't seen a soul do that since the fifth grade and when I saw it I honestly didn't know it was from Merton because I wouldn't think he would know all the letters in the alphabet, much less be able to count all the way to 26. I'm not kidding, he really is that dumb. It must have taken him all week to figure that out and I just got mad enough to kick myself after I sat down and worked it all out.

The school bus is stuck somewhere, I bet that's what it is, backed off in a ditch somewhere and I have to sit here in the rain waiting all day for it with that Merton standing across the road just getting soaking wet and waiting for me to look up so he can start talking to me. If I had known, I could have stayed at the house but then I might have missed it and I would have been mud from head to toe before I got there and late to boot. My scarf is so wet that there are just whole drops dripping off the end and after I even ironed the lace separate down the front of my blouse. And there is something over my head in the tree because I hear it rattle in the branches and the water is dumping down like somebody is up there pouring it out of a bucket. I would think it was Merton if I didn't know he was across the road so it must be a squirrel. I hear Merton's silly laugh now, he can see something funny in nothing if you ask me. I just felt every last bit of the curl go out of my hair after I slept all night on those rollers and it's streaking across my face like somebody broke an egg on my head.

"Hey, Rachel! Don't you know enough to come in out of the rain?"

I look up at Merton and that darn squirrel starts running up the limb right over my head and washes off every last speck of anything I had put on my face. There just isn't any getting any wetter.

"Merton Hopkins, you see me sitting under a tree and not right out there catching it and I don't fully see how there is any place to go in out of the rain and aren't you someone to tell me about not having enough sense."

I try to see if he is laughing at me and I just know I'm looking like a wet dog. I can see the red lights of the bus blinking down the road and Merton is walking across towards me . . . like he's raking leaves with his feet, that's the way Merton Hopkins walks.

"I heard Mr. Stokes tell you not to plan on coming back to school until you got your hair cut and it sure hasn't been cut," I say.

"You know what I seen?" Merton says and pulls a strand of his black hair down to the end of his nose. "I seen old man Stokes go walking out in the wind the other day and what you know, his hair is longer than mine."

"Oh Merton, you know that's not so. Why he hasn't got enough hair to cover his skin up."

"No, it's the truth. He just grows it all on back so he can comb it up front over his hollow spot."

"It's a bald spot, not a hollow spot and if there's anybody got a hollow spot in the head it's you, Merton Hopkins, and you are fixing to get put out of school for good."

"You got black streaks running off your eyes."

Oh, he could have gone all day long and not said that. I take a Kleenex out of my pocketbook and wipe under my eyes and it just gets black as tar and it said on the card that it was waterproof. That was why I bought it, so I could go swimming and it would stay on and they would think my lashes were black. Honestly my eyelashes look like they were put on the wrong person, like they should have been on a white rabbit or an albino or something. I just wanted so much for my eyes to show up on stage today. I bet if you were to get at a distance I wouldn't have any face at all, at least that's what Merton said one day when I was walking up to him but he's likely as not got weak eyes and isn't smart enough to know it. I would just love to knock that grinning Merton up beside the head. I would just turn around and go back home this very minute if it wasn't the day my home ec project was due, I would. I wouldn't even go to the tryouts for the ninth grade show and just let Rosey Bell go ahead and get the part of the butterfly. She thinks she's got it anyway.

I reach in my pocketbook for my sun glasses but when I feel them, my finger goes right through one of the eye glasses. I don't wear them two times before I bust them. I would have had to say I had pink eye anyway, anybody who'd go stumbling around in the rain in sun glasses. I just know my face is ruint. I take out my compact and start putting powder over the black smudges, now that eyelash stuff decides to be waterproof when it's not where I want it. Every time I try to look up close the glass clouds up so I hold my breath.

"You look like a toad frog."

My breath all comes out and I shut my compact.

"What else nice are you going to say to me today, Merton? Can't you pick something uglier than a toad frog like calling me an old wart toad or something?"

"Wart toad made your face turn red." Then he starts into that laughing again. "Toad frogs ain't ugly, they just got pop eyes."

See what I mean about him, he never knows when to stop and sometimes I wish I was so big I could just beat him to a speck.

The bus stops and all those silly lights come on to stop traffic as if there's going to be any traffic on this road. Maybe if I sit on the outside of the seat Merton will go somewhere else but I ought to know better than that since I've tried it fifty times and all Merton does is crawl over me. Sometimes I'm almost glad when he doesn't go to school, at least I get a little peace and quiet. Maybe they'll just kick him out for good soon. He's just waiting to turn sixteen anyway so he can quit legal.

"I hear you are going to be the butterfly in the play."

"Merton, just as loud as you please. Now don't go and talk that all over because sure as everything if you do, Rosey Bell will get it and then I'll be embarrassed to tears."

"She ain't as pretty as you."

"Well, everybody don't think like you do, Merton Hopkins. There's some people who think redheads are prettier than anybody."

"I ain't never seen no redheaded butterfly."

"You just tell me when you've seen a blonde-headed butterfly, or any kind of headed butterfly for that matter. Besides her hair isn't natural. I saw in town what she colored it with and you can see it in the roots if you look good. I've known Rosey since she was little and her hair was brown as a mole before she started that coloring in the sixth grade and her name was Fanny. She changed her name and her hair over the summer and thought there weren't anyone who was going to notice any difference and she would go two weeks not talking to anybody who called her Fanny."

"I think Fanny is the best name for her."

"Well I do too."

"I bet you don't for the same reason I do."

"What do you mean?"

"I mean she sure has got a big one if you take the rest of her into account."

"Merton, that was ugly. And she'll be sorry too because my Mama said that the girls who fill out too soon are most inclined to get fat before their time."

"She goes walking down the hall looking like two little pigs fighting under a blanket."

Merton is laughing at himself now. He says that about everybody, at least everybody with a big tail and he thinks he's the funniest thing alive.

"I've already planned how I'm going to make my costume," I say, "if I am to get the part that is. I'm going to make it in home ec class and if I can save enough money I'm going to make it out of real organdy. I don't want any crepe paper costume like I had to have at Christmas, not with everybody around pulling on it till it's all stretched out of shape."

That ought to shut Merton up for a while. He won't say anything to that, not after what he did Christmas when he was supposed to be back there in charge of pulling the curtain and he stepped on the back of my holly costume and tore it so bad I had to back clean off the stage. It was a good thing for me I decided to wear bermudas under it just in case or I would have just died. And that Fanny Bell going out there dressed as a Christmas bell, thinking they gave her the part because of her red hair and her last name. Well, though I wouldn't say it to her face, I think they gave it to her because of her shape which is certainly nothing to be proud of. And then she got the boy doing the program to make sure her name was put down as Rosey instead of Fanny like it really is. I honestly wouldn't name a cow Fanny Bell.

"Oh, for goodness sake!"

Merton's big foot just landed in my lap.

"If you had been born with feet like that, you'd go stepping on the wrong things too!" he says.

"Merton, put your dirty old foot on the floor. You got mud all over my dress."

I shove his foot off my lap and he turns his face out the window. See, that's why he's been so quiet. He was still thinking about stepping on my costume because I told him when he did it, I'd never speak to him again. Now he's pretending his feelings are hurt because he knows that's the only way he can get me to be nice to him. The truth is, that I don't mind Merton so much in the summer when I don't have to be seen with him but when school starts I'd just as soon not know him. There is never any telling what crazy thing he is going to do next. He is really one for picking at you and teasing but if he ever thinks he really did something bad wrong, he'll worry about it forever. I've known that since we were just in the fifth grade together when I was just turned ten and was already getting bumpy faced and worried that I was going to be the ugliest thing alive, because I was the worst cottontop you've ever seen. That was when Merton told me he knew how to make me beautiful.

He told me he was going to give my hair a mud treatment that he had read about on this jar that said "For Beautiful Women Only," and it was guaranteed to make my hair stay curled forever and I could wear the mud for a hat he figured until it came time to take it off. To this day I don't know for sure if he did it for meanness but that Merton had me sitting down there by the pond not moving a muscle while he was piling mud on my head. Then he went running off and told me to wait and I thought he won't never coming back and that it really was just another one of his stunts when he came back with a bunch of black-eyed Susans and stuck them all around in the mud on my head. By this time the mud had started drying and was about to pull my hair out. That was when Merton told me to bend over and look at my pretty hat and I declare I think he did think it was pretty. I saw me for a second in the water with a big head with things sticking out all over it then splash the whole works went toppling over and liked to have yanked my head bald.

I must have scrubbed my hair twenty times before I didn't feel grit down at the roots and by the time I'd finished, if I ever was to have curly hair, I wouldn't again. Now I know that just sounds like Merton really made a monkey out of me and I've been saying all the time he was the stupid one, but I'm still thinking that Merton might have thought it would make me pretty. The reason I have for that is he never did laugh at me after he had done it, in fact I thought he was going to cry and just start running when he saw the terrible mess he'd made of me. And if it had been on purpose, I'm still figuring he would have made fun of me.

With all his scrambling to get on the bus, Merton will be the last one out when it comes time to get off. You ask him why he has to get by the window and he'll say he wants to see where we're going just like we were going to the ocean or something and he knows good and well we pass the same things every day. I can't even remember when they changed the billboards. Merton will try to read the signs and you can see why he's still in the seventh grade. I have tried to tell him fifty times that it's E-s-s-o not 3-s-s-o, and he still thinks that 7-up spells Zup. He tries to read everything he sees out that window out loud but you just see if you can get him to crack a school book. He just doesn't care I guess. He doesn't ever get excited over anything at school.

Sometimes I wish I could be like that because I can as good as tell you right now that come time for me to try out for the play and my stomach will just feel like it's going to cave right in and I'll fall in behind it. If I didn't go through my part so many times in my head first, I bet I could just walk out and say my part and do my dance and look back at the people out front and quit thinking of them looking at me. That's the trouble. Every time I go to practice in my mind I see myself up there and it's like I'm going out in the audience watching me and it is easy as everything. But when the real time comes to do it, I'm trying to see who's watching me through the lights and I talk too fast so I can get it over with quick. It worries me to death when I got no idea in this world of what I look like and I know all those people out front do know. If only it was just in front of a mirror like at home instead of people, you know what I mean? When you do something wrong, like in this dance I've got to do, you say no and do it over again until it looks right.

I can hear Merton's head thumping against the window and when I look at him, he won't even look at me. Honestly when I hurt Merton's feelings it's like somebody drained the life out of him, just as limp as a dishrag and any normal person would feel his brains shaking out on that window. You could hit Merton in the head with a brick and not raise a swelling, you could. And he's not just hardheaded in the skin; he's hardheaded inside too. He wouldn't do a thing a teacher asked him to do if he thought the world was coming to an end. The last time I asked him what he planned to do with himself, you know what he said? Raise pickles! At first I thought maybe he was dumb enough to think they grew in jars when he said to me, "They'll give me two dollars a bushel for all the cucumbers I can raise long as I don't let them get no longer than three inches before I pull them." But you can't tell Merton anything, he is always trying to raise some fool thing. He's got it in his head that he'll be filling bushels with regular sized cucumbers not three inch ones. Why it'd take an acre to get one bushel I bet. It's always raising, just try to tell him that there are some things in this world that come about without being planted in dirt.

One time he decided to raise drinking gourds and I don't know a soul who would use a drinking gourd to drink out of if he had one. When I told Merton that everybody I knew used at least a tin dipper if not a glass, he decided to make bird houses out of the gourds but couldn't make the birds decide they wanted to live in one of them. I remember the time he got all these fancy herb seeds out of an order in an oatmeal

box. That was the year his cow broke loose and ate them all up then got bloated and he was wondering if it won't a good thing, that maybe all that parsley and sage and stuff would have killed a person. Now his pumpkin crop was really something, you have never seen such pumpkins. I mean they would near about glow in the dark. They looked like the kind you would find in some little kid's book, painted bright orange by somebody who has never seen a pumpkin and makes pigs pink and apples red all over. Well, they were too small for jack-o-lanterns, Merton never paid any attention to what it said on the package—actual size: five inches through and that they were "ornamental." I read the package to him even and said don't you know what ornamental means and he said sure you hang ornaments on the Christmas tree which meant he was about half a hair right and there was no use in the world to try to finish explaining to him so I just let it go. Then he tried to sell them to people for pies and everybody told him they weren't a proper color to be eaten, that they must certainly be poisoned. He slopped the hogs with them until the hogs got sick of pumpkin and rolled them out of the trough and they tell it on Merton that he hauled them all down to the trash pile and busted every last one of them. Well, anyway that's Merton. Just yesterday he was going around singing "I love BERRIES in the springtime." I could make a crow white before I could get that straight in his head.

I really would never have spoken to him again after he tore my holly costume if I couldn't make Merton do things that not a soul on this earth would do. I would be walking along with him in the summer and it would be just as sticky hot as it could be and I'd say, Merton, I want that flower up there on that rock and he would go climbing up twenty feet after it, just howling every time he touched one of the hot rocks. Reason I'm reminded of his howling is I sent him up after this passion flower once. I hadn't seen one of those passion flowers up close since I was a little girl and we were going to the ocean and stopped at one of those roadside places and there was one growing on the girls' privy that I couldn't reach and my daddy wouldn't get it for me which I could understand. Merton said he didn't see the flower up there that day we were walking from the store but I knew it was there because they are hooked onto a long vine and they look like a purple pinwheel because they bloom out flat intead of cupped up and I could see the vine didn't have but one. I was directing Merton to it and he got the idea to snatch down the whole vine but he forgot that was the same vine he was holding to for support with his other hand and when he yanked it loose, he went with it. But you can't hurt Merton; he just let out a yap when he hit and pulled half the hill down on top of himself.

You should have seen my flower once I got it, It was a mess. And just about the stinkingest thing I'd ever smelled. I was cussing at Merton and he said he didn't make it smell, that it won't nothing but a maypop that I almost made him break his neck over and there were thousands of them out in the fields. I did feel a little bad since he had such a time getting it and wished I had said something nice about the flower but it was too late, anyhow I don't think anybody could have said a nice thing about that flower even if they were used to fibbing. Then he tried to show me those thousands out in the fields and I tell you he couldn't find a one after all his big talking and I wanted to know if it really would smell that bad if it wasn't squashed because I wanted to wear it in my hair.

I asked him where in the world he got maypop and he said that was a name for an old tire with cardboard in it that may pop any minute and I said what did it have to do with the flower and he said he didn't know, it was just a maypop. That's the way Merton is. He'll argue until he's blue in the face and not have the slightest notion of what it is he's arguing about.

Merton just groaned and slid down further in the seat. He always does that in the last half mile before school and he'll shut his eyes and be sound asleep before we get there. He's going to really catch it about that hair but I reckon that's why he grew it, so he could get sent home. It's about time for Merton to want to starting planting things. He said yesterday he was going to try grafting this year until he got a tree that would grow apples and pears and plums all at the same time. He did get a pear limb to stick to an apple tree last year but it didn't have any pears . . . just leaves.

It's finally over. After all my worrying, I just went out there and did it but I know I did it a thousand times better at home when the teachers weren't there. And of course there was Merton sitting back there in the auditorium watching me. I don't know why I came back here and sat with him; I just didn't think I could stand to sit down front where all the teachers are.

"You looked good except for that one place you got out of step with the music."

"How do you know whether or not I was in step

with the music. You can't even count out the beats."

"I can too. I could play the drums if I had a set."

Sometimes I just wish Merton wouldn't say anything at all and would just leave me alone. I worry about things enough without him making it worse. He never knows when he's said enough; now I've got to worry all afternoon that I was out of step. Rosey comes up next. I know she's scared good because I saw her backstage. They had to tell her to get quiet twice because she was talking so loud. I wish Merton would go outside; there are so many times when I just wish he wasn't around or didn't know me or something.

"Hey, Rosey's next." That was Merton and he said it so loud two of the teachers who are down front turned around. Honestly, Merton just doesn't know any better.

"How do you know she's next?" I whisper.

"Cause I can see her over there poking her head around the curtain waving at somebody."

The piano starts playing again, The Waltz of the Flowers is the only thing Miss Tripp knows but that doesn't mean she can play it the same way twice. There goes Rosey out; Miss Tripp didn't make a mistake on the introduction for her like she did on mine, how can you be expected to stay in step if the piano player can't even keep the time. Rosey was in my dance class; we both had a year of tap, ballet, and acrobatics but she didn't have such a big tail then. She was just sort of high pockets. I knew she would do the same dance as me since that's the only one we learned all the way through before we quit taking. She never could do a leap without sounding like an elephant when she lands.

"Ka-whomp, ka-whamp, ka-thump, ka-thud!"

That was Merton again and one of the teachers turns around but I don't look at Merton this time; I just hit him with my elbow.

"Hey look!"

Merton yelled that good and loud. The teachers up front get out of their chairs and go to the edge of the stage. I thought sure they were coming to throw us out and just ruin my chances for good but . . . "Merton, where's Rosey?"

"She fell down!"

"She didn't fall over the edge, did she? Where is she?"

"Behind the curtain. She got her foot caught up in it and crawled over behind it."

I heard one of the teachers call to see if she was all right but she didn't answer. She's crying that's why, I can hear her crying real loud. One of the teachers has gone up there and I can see her get Rosey to her feet.

"Now she'll limp. I bet she'll limp and try to make them feel sorry for her and think something happened to her besides just being clumsy footed. Look at her pretending to limp, Merton."

They just told Miss Tripp at the piano something and she folded up her music. I feel my heart go away inside my chest, like a hole just popped inside me.

That means the tryouts are over. Rosey's not going to go back and do the dance all the way through. She's giving up.

"Rachel Troppin?"

"Yes Ma'am, Miss Tripp." I feel myself get up and start down to the front of the auditorium.

"You will be our butterfly then."

"Yes, Miss Tripp. Thank you very much."

"Rosey is going to be all right. She just turned her ankle but I don't think it would be wise for her to plan on dancing in the play with a weak ankle."

I see Rosey now sitting on the steps. She is still sniffing but smiling funny like. Her ankle is kind of swollen. The way Miss Tripp smiles at her, I bet I know what she did. She told Rosey she would have had the part to get her to stop crying and then told her she had better let me have it. That's what she did, I bet. "You'll be our butterfly then" she says to me like I wouldn't have been anyway.

"And Rachel dear, before rehearsals start let me make it clear to you that you shouldn't bring your boyfriend with you unless he sits on the very back row and stays absolutely quiet."

"Oh, Miss Tripp. Merton's not my boyfriend. He just follows me around because he lives near me. He most certainly is not my boyfriend."

"Well, I don't care who he is, he was with you and he disturbed our tryouts."

"Yes Ma'am, I'll tell him you don't want him here."

The back door just slammed loud; that had to be Merton. Who else hasn't got any more sense than that.

"Goodness!" Miss Tripp says.

Rosey starts trying to get up and Miss Tripp says, "I guess we had better not try to do any more today in all this confusion. Be here tomorrow right after school lets out, Rachel."

"Yes Ma'am."

I run up the aisle to the door. I want to get outside so bad. If I don't get through the door this second . . . it's still raining. My face must just be burning hot I'm so embarrassed. And there won't be another bus home. I'll have to walk now and Merton has gone on without me. The rain makes my face feel cold but it doesn't feel good even then. I hate to get wet again. But I don't care about my hair any more, it'll just frizz all over anyway. I don't care if my face streaks red and black all over.

There's Merton up ahead. He really did start home without me. I can't tell if he's walking slow so I can catch up or not but I will.

"Merton, wait up!"

He stops but he doesn't turn around.

"Merton, I got the butterfly."

He just starts walking again. When I'm beside him he doesn't even turn to say anything to me. Now what have I done to hurt his feelings?

"Miss Tripp must have told Rosey she would have gotten the part if she hadn't fallen down," I say. "You don't believe she would have, do you Merton?"

"You were glad she fell down."

That sounded scary. That didn't sound like Merton.

"That's not true. I would rather have gotten the part fair and square."

"No, you were glad."

Merton is taking bigger steps now. I can't keep up with him and my throat is getting sore from hurrying so hard. I can see the light spots on his shirt when he swings his arms, he's not rained on there but I feel rained on all over, so much my clothes are hurting me. He is so far ahead of me now, he's not walking with me anymore. He's walked off and left me.

Over the ditch . . . he's taking the short cut over the ditch through the woods path. I don't want to walk by myself; it looks dark already with the rain.

"Merton, please wait up for me! I don't want to walk all the way by myself."

Merton stops at the edge of the woods.

"Well, come on."

I'm getting cold. That's not right, it's just not right for him to be like that to me. He's just being plain mean.

"Merton, you know I can't get over that ditch."

"I seen you jump that far before." Then he looks hard at me and looks real mean. "I seen you jump farther than that up on that stage."

"But there wasn't a hole there, Merton. Don't make me stand here and freeze. Please come back over and walk the road with me. I'm scared to try to jump it."

"I want to see you jump over that ditch if you want to walk with me."

My eyes are burning now and I couldn't jump, I couldn't jump if the hole wasn't even there.

"You want to see me fall, Merton."

I start back up the road. I would give up my butterfly part to be home and dry, I would. I really would if I could be home right this very second with dry clothes on and dry shoes and socks and be warm in my own house and not on this road all by myself. And Merton's turned mean to me. He is just going to go off and leave me and not care a bit if something should happen to me. He won't care a bit.

"He give me three weeks to get it cut."

"What! Merton, you scared the stuffings out of me, sneaking up on me like that! I didn't even hear you."

"He give me three weeks because I told him I had to make the money for a haircut or my mama would cut it with a bowl."

"Merton, that's a big fib. I bet you got money enough in your pocket right this very minute for a haircut if you wanted one."

"Yep."

"Merton you really *are* going to get thrown out for good."

Merton sticks his hands in his back pockets and I see that dry spot under his arm is still there. He didn't listen to one word I said about getting thrown out.

"Hey Rachel, what you think if I grafted a maypop onto a rosebush? Do you reckon it might smell good?"

FOUR HOUR THUNDER

By William Trotter

. . . no other sport—and very few other human activities—involves the wild elements of automobile racing. The driver is engaged in an exploration of the outer boundaries of man's ability to deal with the machines which dominate his life.—Leon Mandel, Editor, *Car and Driver*.

STROPHE ONE: "GENTLEMEN, START YOUR ENGINES!"

Seventy thousand people make a lot of noise, especially when they are screwed up to a high pitch of excitement. They are all on their feet and suddenly there is a silence, a kind of wild vacuum into which must explode the anticipated Thunder. Heat shivers up from the asphalt and shatters in waves off the cars, forty-four of them, now motionless to the eye. But if metal can be said to be alive, then the cars are like the crowd: reined-back, taut. Overhead the loudspeakers grate into life with a few throat-clearing crackles. Then comes that single sentence which will be the only completely audible announcement of the entire afternoon: "Gentlemen, start your engines!"

And suddenly there is The Thunder. It shakes the concrete and momentarily stuns the mind. Forty-four of the most powerful terrestrial engines ever built crash into life. Waves of hot, gritty sound wash up from the asphalt. There begins a formalized passage of time-motion, a series of formulated actions that will be bounded by The Thunder for the next four hours. All that is human, all that is flowing within the track, the grandstands, the apocalyptic swarm of the Infield, will be measured now against the dimensions of The Thunder. The Sound will blast apart all oral communication. Its ebb and flow around the one and three-eighths mile track will establish a cyclic rhythm of titanic power. In time it will infiltrate the cells of the brain, and the muscles will vibrate to its fury, and every driver in every car will be one with The Thunder: organs, muscles, burned nerve-endings, the calculations of the mind—all must serve The Thunder and ride its gigantic currents and sense, from microsecond to microsecond, the inhuman nuances of its moods, the subtleties of its vastness. And those who watch from the storm's-eye of the pits, who crouch against the illusory barrier of the guard rails and breathe in The Thunder's hot breath, must hope that it can be tamed and ridden.

But in that first instant, when the shock wave is like a giant hot fist, it does not seem that human beings can measure themselves against it and survive.

ANTISTROPHE ONE: ANTICIPATIONS: THE LAND OF THE ARR-AH-CEE COLA AND THE MOON PIE:

When you come from North Carolina and you've been away for two years and you come back and have occasion to travel to South Carolina, there is a kind of double cultural shock involved in crossing that state line. When you are going to the Labor Day races at Darlington, the condition is worsened and the perceptions heightened by the knowledge that you will be partaking in what amounts to a mass ritual performed each year by a vast cult of which you are not a part, not really (Or *are* you, you transplanted mutha, some insistent whisper will say as the day burns on in its strange equation of formality and chaos . . .) If you are all the above things and you also know that George Wallace has selected Darlington for one of his Appearances, and, knowing the South in general and South Carolina rednecks in particular, you are painfully conscious of a nagging hope that someone will redress an accumulated cosmic injustice by shooting George Wallace in what passes for his brain (J.F.K. plus R.F.K. plus M.L.K. equals maybe 1/250th G.W. on the current assassination market), and you are also aware that your physical appearance is, by Wallace folks' standards, that of an outside-agitating-anarchist-beatnik-pinko-hippy-pot-smoking-commie-rat-pervert (no haircut in, let's see now, eight or nine weeks . . .); if you are in that position, the border crossing from North to South Carolina seems fraught with perils other than those of the lethal weekend traffic. This is where you come from, and no amount of city-living or literary polish can obliterate a sense of the haggard doom that lies, centuries-old, steeped into the earth on either side of the highway.

Breakfast in a borderline highway cafe: something ineffably familiar about the rural southern grunginess of the interior, the universal gauntness of the waitresses. Lots of race-bound cars parked in front. Lots of Wallace stickers on the bumpers. Inside, a familiar drowse of conversation. Two highway cops give you the hairy eyeball as you order your pancakes and bacon. You brush back your hair under that up-against-the-wall stare and gratefully touch the press cards and pit passes pinned to your shirt. The conversation around you is heavily larded with references to the race and to "Gawge." Mental note: when writing the article, *do* refrain from "*race*-ist" puns about G.W.

The traffic gets thick about twenty miles from the speedway. Bumper-to-bumper, the cars crawl slowly down the dirt road into the back entrance. Ahead is a station wagon plastered with Wallace stickers and filled with shirtless beer-guzzling young men. Through a break in the dusty pines, comes the first glimpse of the grandstands: a severe oblong reared against a tight, hot sky. Then the car moves through the first gates and there is a feeling of immersion into a moist, swarming torrent of humanity. A lean state cop with a turkey's stringy neck and a look of mild insanity in his eyes takes the first of a series of passes and waves you into the Infield. Beer cans crunch under the tires. Across the Infield and up to the pit-area gates. Credentials are examined and more passes taken. The groundlings in the Infield glower enviously as your car grinds through the gates and into the pit area. You park and step out into the oven heat from which there will be no escape: pouring down in a solid shaft from the sky and angled up in vibrant sheets from underfoot.

QUALIFYING LAPS: SOME THINGS YOU NEED TO KNOW IF
YOU DON'T ALREADY:

Automobile racing (the overall classification includes motorcycles, dragsters, the Grand Prix big boys, Volkswagen competitions, demolition derbies and dune-buggies) is now statistically the second most popular sport in the nation, and its myriad devotees and investors look forward to a time when it will be Number One. In 1967 there were 40 million paid admissions to races. Seat prices range from $2.50 for your friendly neighborhood dirt-track, to $25.00 for a box seat at a Grand Prix spectacular. Average admission is about ten bucks. Do your own computing as to the total sums involved in 40 million paid admissions, and you will get a glimmer of the fortunes made and broken behind the scenes.

The overall structure of the racing establishment is a Byzantine labyrinth of hierarchies-within-hierarchies. Money, technical data, influence and prestige ebb and flow, filtered through the often ephemeral consciousnesses of Ford, Chrysler, G.M., NASCAR, Firestone, Goodyear, Standard Oil, *et al*. The echoes of a crack-up at Darlington may, within hours, resonate deep within the bowels of Dow Jones. The maneuvering and sometimes literal wheeler-dealing that surrounds the racing world is a blend of almost arcane ritual and ultra-modern technological main-lining. The security surrounding a new tire compound, for example, is roughly equivalent to that enveloping a CIA plot to liquidate some tainted, minor-league Prime Minister in Upper Volta.

A big-winning car can be sliced up among the various firms whose products have seen it through the season. The tires go to Goodyear or Firestone and will be seen in due course on TV commercials throughout the land. The gas tank goes to Pure or Shell so that you, dear consumer, can be persuaded that, because super-premium ultra-octane Zappoflash enabled Fearless Danny Dingbat to drive for five hours at 125 miles-per-hour with an engine worth more than your life savings, it will somehow enable you to get through the Lincoln Tunnel in record time.

The term "stock car" sums it up. "Stock" cars are different from "sports" cars. No one in his right mind would attempt to drive a Le Mans-winning $150,000 Lotus on a typical urban freeway, even if it were financially possible to do so. The "stock" car, though, looks for all its race-time adornments, substantially the same as the cars gleaming in your franchised dealer's showrooms. Stock cars must, by rule, look that way. What's under the hood, of course, is a far cry from the engine in the family sedan, but even so, stock car engines must stay within certain restrictions of cubic size and weight and the internal modifications that make them the children of The Thunder must also stay within the boundaries of a host of technical limitations. As the boys on the Avenue of the Mad would say, "It's the image, baby, the *image!*" that sells the cars. After a big race, showroom sales of the win-

ning model will invariably show a steep rise. One concrete example: the Ford "Starliner" was, nationally, about as big a trend-setter as the Edsel; but, because a Starliner won several big races, its sales in the South were better-than-average for some months. It works like that. Bobby Jo Beauregard Jackson has been saving his gas-station wages for two years; he comes to Darlington and sees Richard Petty ride to victory in a Plymouth Wildebeast, and Bobby Jo goes out next morning and heads straight for his Plymouth dealer. Somehow, for him, the driver's seat of his new, factory-normal car, is redolent with a faint pride of shared heroism. When he goes out after work to pick up high school girls at the local drive-in, he can break the ice thusly: "My new car? Yeah, it's the same one Petty drove at Darlington. Wanna go for a ride in it?" It works, some places, more often than you might think.

Stock car racing is a national sport. You will even find surly Bronx street hoods gossiping about the newest three-barreled carburetors and imperiling the after-dark streets with their own hopped-up vehicles. But you will not find anything like the intensity, the true *aficionado* loyalties and passions, of southern stock car fans anywhere but in the South itself. They may not have made it through the sixth grade, but they know the engines, the drivers, the characteristics of the tracks, the past records of the best races, the numerical and monetary odds for and against every aspect of a given race from the length of the pit stops to the number of beers Driver X can drink the night before without jeopardizing his chances in the morning. They *know*. And despite attempts by NASCAR and other powers-that-be to give the sport a new image of "class" (Frank Sinatra has even recorded a song about it . . .) the sport remains essentially the sport of the southern low and lower-middle-class white man.

PIT STOP NO. 1: "GODAMIGHTYDAMN! HE'S THE GREATEST
THING SINCE DON KWIK-ZOTE!!"

Given the importance of the race to all true stock car fans, it was going to take something special to redirect the excitement of the pre-race ceremonies. That something was George Wallace. That Strom Thurmond was going to be there too, seemed too much a conjunction of interests to be coincidence. These were George's and Strom's "folks" and where else could they find so many of them within demagoging distance? No; given the political climate of this 1968 September, it was inevitable that one or both of them should be here.

The crowd knew it was going to get two-for-one: the race itself, and a swift injection of political meth-edrine, and it hungered. As soon as the speakers' platform was wheeled out in front of the main grandstand, the crowd got restless. Viewed from across the track, the stands blurred into a single rippling wall of humanity, monocromatic and featureless except for the seasoning of da-glo orange banners, posters, and straw hats that bore the name "Wallace." These were now

Photographs by Walter Charnley

being waved and flung about in the air, giving the stands the appearance of a million firecrackers popping off at once. Someone sang the "Star-Spangled Banner" over the PA system and it was the first time one had heard that usually innocuous hymn tinged with menace.

There were a number of functionaries lined up to speak, but the crowd wanted none of it. There came a chant, ragged at first, then unified and insistent: "We want Wallace! We want Wallace!" One harassed speaker broke off his prepared remarks with a benevolent shrug and stepped down, saying: "Okay, then—you're gonna git him!" Wild cheering.

There was a commotion behind the speakers' stand. A phalanx of cops appeared with bobbing Smokey-the-Bear hats of the highway patrol ringing the center. Somewhere in the middle of that was George Wallace. The cops spread out around the rear of the podium. Highway patrolmen, state police, security guards in mufti. It was hard at first to distinguish between the U. S. Secret Service guards and the members of Wallace's private Gestapo. They all wore sunglasses and had blond crewcuts and monumentally forgettable faces. The differences revealed themselves slowly. The Secret Service agents fanned out at a moderate distance, sunglasses scanning both the near-crowds and the distant elevations where the sun might glint on the barrel of a sniper's rifle. Not that George had much to fear: in this setting, before this crowd, he was safer than he was at home in bed. Still, the Secret Service men went through the motions, occasionally speaking unheard things into small walkie-talkies. Wallace's own guards stayed closer to him, eyes resting more

on Der Fuehrer than on the crowds around him. They were scrawnier than the government men, more rigid, fingers closer to the trigger. The Secret Service men were dressed in bland, conservative, but respectable business suits; the Wallace gunsels looked to have purchased their suits off the back rows at Robert Hall.

Fifty yards away was a good vantage point, but one naturally wished to get closer to the Action. One was prevented by several local cops. Press credentials were bluntly ignored. Jaundiced looks at one's long hair and the glint of a passing question in the cops' eyes: What're *you* doin' here, punk? The state cops were either tendony with big adam's apples and bad, equine teeth, or Bull Conner beefslabs with terrific

paunches taut over their pistol belts. A man's flesh gets pulled, over his years, toward the center of his gravity —in this case, the heavy .38's riding on the hip.

Strom and George were chatting together behind the stand now. Two down-home country boys exchanging sly, aww-sheeeit, grins.

Standing next to George and Strom were two strange apparitions: a beauty queen—one never did catch exactly what her title was—in a gold dress with a veritable helmet of brass-blonde hair, and a lanky man costumed—in a full Confederate uniform and carrying an immense stars-and-bars flag that thudded in the fitful wind like a sluggish bullwhip.

The crowd was on its feet. Strom mounted the plat-form and reverently took off his hat. Tufts of white hair blowing in the wind, a look of: these-are-my-people-God-bless-'em humility softening his crafty face. He looked like a tobacco auctioneer who's just been informed that he has lung cancer. The Folks loved ol' Strom, all right, and the applause was warm. But there was an edge of impatient hysteria threat-ening to break through, and Strom knew better than to try and upstage the Main Event. He welcomed the crowd, told 'em how good it was to see 'em all again, hinted that he was still lookin' after 'em up there in Washington, waved paternally, and stepped down.

The President of NASCAR strode vigorously up to the microphones. He was wearing a white tie with "WALLACE" printed down the length of it in da-glo orange. He motioned imperiously for silence and got it. Then he bent dramatically into the mikes and said:

"I just got one thing to say to you folks: George Washington founded the Union . . ." (dramatic pause; The Folks know what's coming . . .) ". . . and George Wallace *is gonna save it!!!*"

One's mind had time to form the question "For whom?" and then the crowd gave answer with a single howling roar. The Confederate flag did hand stands in the air. Da-glo exploded in the grandstands like cold napalm as people whooped, rebel-yelled, leaped up and down, threw hats into the air, and pounded one another on the back.

George Wallace slowly mounted the podium, savor-ing the moment, knowing that some echo of this grass-roots howl was going to reach Washington and curdle the ear-wax in some very high places.

The pandemonium grew louder, wilder. Then, it struck that there was something in it all of an especi-ally macabre *dèjà vu*. The uniforms around the po-dium, the hoarse raw hysteria of the crowds, the vast scale of the setting. The thought kicked into the con-sciousness like a jack-boot: Nüremberg, 1938.

Here he was, folks. The Messiah. The voice of all the people who considered the twentieth century to be a personal affront. And yet, how petty he seemed in comparison to the Austrian corporal! There was some-thing about Hitler that removed him from normal human dimensions: the scale of his perversity, the yardstick of his deeds, were Evil in a Wagnerian di-mension. Here was the closest thing yet to America gone Fascist, and the worst that could be said about it was that it partook of the meaner qualities of a Klan rally and a backwoods revival meeting. Here was re-lease for all the most murderous and mindless currents in our national soul and even the fear it stirred was blurred by contempt and the laughter of the absurd; its potential for ultimate horrors was masked by a slightly unreal banality. How could it be taken *seri-ously?*

George did not use the occasion for what he might have considered a major policy address. He knew it would not be too politie to steal too much of The

Thunder. The race was what the crowd had come to see, and George was willing to let himself serve as icing on the cake. No remarks about "soo-doe innal-lechals" or briefcase-totin' bureaucrats or how the national interests could be served by running over hippies with your car or jailing the Supreme Court. Just a few well-drawled homilies about how good it is to see y'all today, and how, next time Ah come down this way, it'll be all the way from the White House. We gonna *win* in November, you hear!!?

Wheee-haaaa!! You bet, George!!

When he finished, the uproar dwarfed anything previous. They had seen Him and heard Him. He was their voice, their White Knight—he had stood up and proclaimed what they all knew: that the confusions, ambiguities and maddening changes of the times could be reversed by them—the Little People, as they, and He, liked to call themselves with a kind of depraved smugness that thinly masked their terror of one day waking up and having to face the reality that they were no longer very important to the world, that they must yield and change or be swallowed up—not through persecution or legislation, for that would be too simple for the dynamics of this century—but simply through impotence. Already, the niggers were forging ahead of them, and when that happened, there would be no one, no one in the whole nation, that they could feel superior to, smarter, better, or richer than, and so He was their last and loudest hope, and his glandular rhetoric their last shrill justification for a way of life that had outlived itself by a century. For a passing moment, then, knowing them as only a native could, one felt pity and sorrow.

For they were good people, most of them. They were born hard and they had had to work hard. They had names like Stubbs and Blackwelder and Turnipseed; they were dirt farmers and mechanics and drugstore owners and shoe salesmen and millhands; they fed their families decently and cheated on their wives a lot less than they wanted to and a lot of them were good Baptists and use-green-wood Calvinists; and in all the recent wars, they had been the cannon fodder of the armies of the nation that now no longer needed them; and they were the victims of a century that seemed bent on their bewilderment and extermination.

So one felt sadness and pity, because one knew many of them, and one liked their strength, their capacity for endurance; the innocent tenacity of their ignorance had sometimes seemed refreshing. How vital they were at their best; how dismal and primitive at their worst.

Wallace moved now along the rim of the pit area, mobbed by well-wishers and heavily guarded. The cops were grinning like school kids. He was their man, too. People pressed forward eagerly as he drew near, extending their hands for a touch.

"Hey, hey, George, over here!"

"Hey, Mr. President! We're with ya, all the way!"

"Yaahooo!! South's gonna RIIIISE again!"

Dialogue overhead as Wallace drew near: "Hey, did you see Him on TV yesterday?" "Naw—what'd he say?" "Aww, shit, man, he was smartern' hell! All them newsmen tried to trap him into some kind of fancy talk about foreign policy and all that stuff—ol' George wouldn't take the bait, nossir! He wasn't gonna let 'em trick him with any doubletalk! He wouldn't even *answer* none of them questions! Man, he's a smart cat!"

And so Wallace passes. There is nothing truly remarkable about the face. The hair is slicked back with no real part, thinning from the forehead aft. The brows are heavy and sharp, tilting inward toward a large, blunt, slightly bent nose. The mouth is belligerent, even in the throes of a satisfied smile; the chin pugnacious and round. Only the eyes are frightening. They are the eyes of a humanoid pig: self-righteous smugness oozes from the corners like phony tears. The gaze is shifty, guarded, quick; in a word: cunning. The eyes belong to a man who has reached a prominence that no rational standards would judge him fit to occupy; the eyes, also, of a man who has almost convinced himself that he really belongs where he is, and whose vanity and soullessness have triumphed over the knowledge of his essential littleness. Eyes of a man who has begun to brick-in the weaknesses of his ego with the piety of Power.

George Wallace passes, and someone runs around in his wake with his right hand outthrust, saying over and over again: "Hey, how'd you like to shake the hand that shook the hand of . . ." There are plenty of takers.

LAPS: MILE 1-MILE 150:

The Thunder is fifteen minutes old.

The Sound vibrates hugely behind you, over across the swarming Infield, and the straight and two turns of track on the pit side are momentarily empty of cars. The Sound swells to your right and you turn and see them coming out of the far turn where the bank is so treacherous that, somehow, it must be traversed single-file by all the cars. Bellowing and wavering in a cloud of gritty grey fumes and wavering heat, they slide ponderously in and out of line, the right fenders sometimes just barely kissing the safety wall for a passing lick of balance and stability—love pats at one-sixth the speed of sound.

Into the straight before the main grandstands: two, three, four abreast, the formation shifting from instant to instant, The Thunder coming wide-open now and shaking the concrete with its fury. The instant when they pass is total and suspended in time and the cars become The Thunder itself.

You crouch behind the guard rail at the start of the near turn, where the asphalt begins to ascend in a brutally graceful curve until the cars, perilously locked into its apogee, will be angled forty-five degrees or more above horizontal and the chances of an accident at their statistical best. Between you and the track is ten feet of brownish earth and the single crinkled ribbon of guard rail.

The Thunder strains into the turn and you realize how flimsy that guard rail is, how savagely quick an accident can occur, how lethal is the momentum of an extra-heavy automobile out of control at 120 mph, and you remember suddenly the small print on the pit passes: "Guests privileged to enter the pit areas, do so at their own risk."

The roar recedes except for two stragglers, one already bent in the bumpers, laboriously struggling to catch up with the race. There have already been some mishaps on the far side of the track. You don't have to see them or hear about them over the loudspeakers —which are seldom audible in any case—to know they have happened: the crowd knows, all seventy thousand, because it is wired-up to The Thunder and catches the slightest alteration of its basic frequency. Sensing it, the crowd will be on its feet as one man and, standing lower than the grandstands, you can feel the line of their sight passing over you toward some unseen incident a mile away. The cars come into the far turn again, the Sound bigger somehow than before, a wild, spoiling, put-up-your-dukes throatiness is trembling in The Thunder as they come through the straightaway, bones in their teeth. One battered car heads for the pits, peeling off from the track at eighty mph and lurching toward its pit crew with clumps of oily smoke coughing from its exhausts. Scratch one.

Something happens as the rest pass the straight and begin their drift into the far turn. The formation loosens, becomes ragged. The Thunder seems to wobble and fluctuate uncertainly. And then you know it's going to happen.

You know, five seconds before it happens. That change in the Sound, that electric realization zapping through the crowd, and your eyes focus on the worst spot on the turn, at the highest bank, where the asphalt has begun to look soft under the heat of the constant friction.

Your eyes are not your own; they become part of the crowd, following its instinctive reaction, and so you not only know it's about to happen, but you know where and, a split second before there is any real sign, you know which car. *That* one.

Even as you pick it out, you see a tremor pass through the metal. The wheels wobble and the first awful plumes of screaming smoke jet back from each tire. It is all happening, it seems, in perfect slow silence now, and once you see that smoke, the rest follows with the icy inevitability of a Greek drama. The driver's arms rigid against the bucking wheel, face contorted, the rear end of the car screams hot smoke, slews up into the gradient. One passing car just shaves by between the hurtling casualty and the far guard rail; the next, and 120-plus mph, rams square into the rear of the derelict, spinning it completely around so that the next car, wobbling wildly to evade the inevitable, bites deep into the front and caroms off into the side of yet another. The first car spins drunkenly

toward the Infield, nicked yet again as it seeks someway OUT of all that speed and fury and murder. The whole crash scene is now streaked with jets of steam and smoke—a radiator explodes like a cloud of thick, dirty snow—the first car slides howling into the dirt and a thin sheet of pale flame sprays back from the mangled hood and lashes the the windshield.

Men are running now. The caution flag goes up and The Thunder lowers its voice for the first time in the afternoon, almost in tribute to the fallen. Sirens and flashing lights. The first car is motionless now, sluggishly burning and dripping streams of oil. Then the driver appears—the angle makes it impossible to see just how he managed to claw his way out of all that tormented metal—his hands waving in the air over his face, legs rubbery, he flails around drunkenly, staggers two steps in no particular direction, then collapses motionless onto the hot, slippery asphalt, his helmet catching the sun like a disc of dirty bronze.

Tow trucks and ambulances gather around the scene like giant insects. The photographers—those vultures by trade—swarm over the guard rail and jockey for position around the fallen man, now so small, so tiny, so very inert against the howling backdrop of the track and the grumbling Thunder, impatient now to be let loose again. Stretcher bearers grope through the crowd and the tender efficiency of their motions over the injured man is reminiscent of some battlefield newsreel. The ambulance jerks away and the tow-truck crew begins to lug the gutted car out of the way. It must all be done quickly: the wrecks removed, the hunks of blackened metal swept clean, the oil slicks covered with sand like blood pools on the floor of an old-time surgery; all done quickly because The Thunder is impatient for a clear track.

And as the clean-up continues, two other drivers walk by—two of the lucky ones whose cars are pranged, to be sure, but who walked away from all that chaos with their limbs and heads intact. They walk together jerkily, stiffly, their mouths ringed with grime. No one tries to speak to them. Newsmen and photographers step aside discreetly as they pass. They pass close. You get one good look into their eyes and you understand why nobody wants to speak to them.

You begin to understand how much potential for death there is within The Thunder.

PIT-STOP NO. 2: "RACE? WHAT RACE??":

In 1950, when the first race was held there, Darlington boasted one twenty-room hotel and not much else. The promoters of that first race had expected maybe a thousand people to show up. By nightfall on the day before the race, there were three or four times that many just milling around outside the fences, with no place to go. Someone had the bright idea of letting them park and camp out in the Infield area inside the inner diameter of the track.

Two decades later, when you speak to a racing buff about the Darlington Infield, he will probably chortle knowingly and a little derisively—the habitues of the Infield may ostensibly *come* to see the race, but by the time the race actually starts, very few of them are in condition to know or care what's happening on the track. Nowadays, there may be as many as 25,000 people crammed into the Infield—nobody bothers to count any more, and there's always room for one more car full. What began in 1950 as a matter of simple expediency has become, for thousands, the hot-damndest social event of the year.

They are, as one unusually hip sports writer has called them, "the Original Speed Freaks." Many of them save their money for weeks to afford admission. They come in gangs and families, in pickup trucks, trailers, campers, buses, battered family sedans. They gather as much as twenty-four hours before the gates are opened, at noon on the Sunday before Labor Day, and by twilight, the Infield is swollen with them. Farmers, college kids, drugstore cowboys, con men, bootleggers, prowling sluts. Tents, tarpaulins rigged

tion of an all-Wasp Resurrection City, tinhorn overnight Las Vegas, and a transplanted outprovince of Appalachia.

The Infielder perambulates all night up and down the rows of vehicles and encampments. The air crackles with popped-open beer cans. Cherry bombs explode. Bottles shatter. Off in a patch of menacing darkness, someone will cackle like a maniac, all night long. Dice rattle under the tent flaps. Inevitably, once or twice a year, someone will run amok with a straight-razor or a saw-toothed rye bottle and the cops will have to make one of their rare forays into the area. Fights break out between Plymouth fans and Ford fans, between farm boys and city slickers, between rivals for the attention of some overdone blonde in toreador pants.

It's a field day for bootleggers, card sharps and revivalists. Past Infield Nights have seen Klan rallies, baptisms, mass brawls, impromptu distilleries, marriages, heart attacks and—legend has it—even a child-

over the tailgates of trucks, creaking observation platforms made from scrap lumber—all these and others less describable, serve as their dwellings.

The local ABC board made an effort to enforce the booze laws . . . once. The local cops don't even bother going inside after dark, contenting themselves with pacing up and down the circumference of the barbed-wire-topped cyclone fence that either keeps the Infielders in or the outsiders out—no one is sure which. Track officials have made lukewarm efforts to clean up the image of the whole affair by advertising it as a kind of family-fun-camp-out-bring-the-kiddies-and-watch-the-race, but the Infielders know what the action is and the whole happening has become the kind of tradition that no promoter in his right mind would try to "clean up" too zealously. The action starts at twilight, the night before the race, and by that time, the Infield has taken on its usual apearance: a combina-

birth or two. At various corners of the swarm, entertainment and business establishments of diverse kinds flourish. There will be several whang-whang country bands, including one named—God's truth—"Herman Hayseed and the Hartzog County Bumpkins"; and, in keeping with the times, a couple of high school hopefuls' rock-&-roll bands, replete with slightly moth-eaten go-go dancers who look like wash-outs from the Pageland Junior High cheerleader squad. A regular attraction is a slick in a black suit with a Bible in one hand standing beside a ragged tent under a sign which reads: "Marriages Performed in Two Minutes—Two Dollars Each! Tent For Rent—$20 an Hour!" In other tents, or, on a classier level, in small mobile-home trailers, are traveling whorehouses that would bring tears of glee to the eyes of Mamie Stover.

It goes like that all night. Dawn bleeds over the Infield hollow-eyed and grim. Viewed from outside

the barbed wire, the place begins to look a little like Auschwitz, with inert or semi-conscious heaps of stained bodies jumbled around and the first bleary dawnlight reflecting on mountains of beer cans and piles of sodden garbage. Then comes the first whiff of brewing coffee, and those survivors not too catatonic to move will begin staggering to whatever vantage points they can find. Places near the fence go first, of course, then the pecking order extends to those who had the foresight to bring enough two-by-fours to rig an elevated platform of some kind. Everyone else— 15,000 of them—is out of luck, since the view from the middle of the Infield is nonexistent and the only way to follow the race from there is by radio. But nobody much cares—it was, it always is, one hell of a party . . .

LAPS: MILE 150-MILE 300:

The Thunder is two hours old.

The sun seems to have singled you out personally. By this point in the race, the heat hovering on the track itself is measured at 120 degrees. Just back from the track, it could not be under ninety-five. The air is heavy with the smell of rubber, gasoline, and lubricants. The pit crews lean against stacks of hot, extra-thick tires, some of them shielding the backs of their necks with kepis made of oily rags.

Under aluminum-roofed sheds, mechanics hustle to get banged-up cars back into the race; even if they don't stand a prayer of placing, there is still the not-inconsiderable lap money to be thought of. An enormous man in black-streaked coveralls, his jowls heaving and streaming sweat, rolls a giant tire into place, blinking sweat and grime from his eyes and bellowing to his assistants: "Come on, goddamn it, MOVE! Git that mutha-fukka back in the race!"

Drivers whose cars have been knocked out stand glumly at the edges of the activity, sucking beers and scowling darkly at the track.

At the far end of the pit areas stands Big John Holman, unlit cigar stub mashed into his grim mouth, a floppy canvas hat shading his big, craggy head from the sun. His driver is running second now; that's good, his expression says, but not good enough.

He is a solitary figure. Nobody small-talks with Big John when he looks like this. Ten years ago, he started his racing business in a converted garage with two mechanics. Today he controls one of the biggest racing and research businesses in the world. He personifies the men who make racing what it is. A blend of Horatio Alger, J. P. Morgan and John Wayne—tough, scrappy, rough-edged, a gentleman when he can afford to be, a tyrant when he has to be, a virtuoso at getting the most out of men and metal that can be gotten. The Thunder is his music, his food, his reason for being. The public image of a racing factory is redolent with tons of grease, of mechanics slopping-about in pools of gunk and clattering away with chaotic piles of tools. Holman's factory, by contrast, is as orderly as the innards of a computer and clean enough for open-heart surgery, every bolt and wrench spotlessly in place. Over it all he watches, orders, manipulates, innovates, and harmonizes with a kind of passionate, manic dedication.

You watch him now, in his element, as much at home in The Thunder as Napoleon was in the smoke of his cannon, remembering how, a couple of years ago, two redneck Plymouth fans—distressed that a Holman Ford had swept the track of all rivals—jumped Big John as he was heading for his motel room and a well-earned bourbon. Holman, in his late forties, dispatched both of them with a punch that could crack an engine block, dusted his hands, and walked calmly on for his drink.

No sir. Nobody messes with this man; as well try to stop one of his cars with your bare hands. He eyes The Thunder as it roars past, his face stony and unreadable. You understand that these are the moments a man like this lives for. There is a vision in his eyes not unlike the vision of an artist: something ineffably private, resistant to definition. This man is the seneshal of The Thunder, and The Thunder has imparted secrets to him alone.

You walk past him, toward the entrance to the Infield. Lots of cops. One hands you the necessary pass, to be surrendered upon re-entry to the pit area. Sidewise glances at your long hair. Off to one side of the gate, stand three Negro highway patrolmen, clannishly together, smiling nervously at nothing in particular. One would give a great deal to know what was in their minds earlier today.

The Infield. Walking down the middle of it, catching impressions on the run: a big suntanned man with a tee-shirt drawing of a Hell's Angels thug in a Nazi helmet crushing a car in one fist, with the legend: "Take a Plymouth Home to Lunch!," another tee-shirt beside him reading: "Sock it to 'em, Ford!", a shirtless man near the fence under a lean-to blanket, his eyes pouched and blood-fogged, beer dripping from his lips, his gaze utterly blank and unfocused, arms bowed and simian; his companion is passed out amid a litter of beer cans, his back exposed to the sun and swollen already into murderous red blisters—every now and then, someone will prod him and a sluggish tremor will run through his frame, but he does not move. Earlier, someone had claimed to have seen a sign on one of the tents reading: George Lincoln Rockwell is buried here . . . somewhere." A cursory search fails to spot the landmark, but there's no reason to doubt that it's in there . . . somewhere.

A quick visit to one of the Infield restrooms, a cinder-block hut that smells like a cross between an abattoir and a tub of rotten head-cheese.

The concession stand smells a little better, but is more crowded, mainly with large sluggish flies. Some wit has posted a sign saying: "Duncan Hines Barfed Here." As well he might if one hamburger be indicative of the culinary standards.

On through the Infield, feet slipping in the beer cans. Two bloat-bellied urchins with crusted chins come stumbling by, one of them waving a tiny Confederate flag. An enormous man with a Wallace straw hat and thick sunglasses sits numbly under a beach umbrella, reading a man's magazine with a cover depicting a scantily clad blonde being tortured by SS men with monocles; the man's ear is wired into a small radio by his side. A farm family nesting in the bed of a pickup truck: the mother, hair bristling with curlers, mouth chipped thinly into her pale cheeks, looks catatonic as the kids swarm over her; the father is playing cards and drinking with some cronies and laughing hugely at something not immediately apparent. Atop a trailer, a group of college-age studs and their dates roll around in the sun like puppies, copping giggly feels and flexing their muscles and trying to look supercool.

This quick jaunt through the Infield reveals a predictable fact: there are few spades here, and those that are, stand close together in odd corners, pretending to watch only the race and doing their best to look like sho-nuff watermelon-eatin' clowns who Know Their Place. No one seems to bother them, but neither is there any noticable intermingling.

Back into the pit area. One pit crew is conferring tensely. They decide to bring their driver in—two of his tires look bad. One mechanic chalks a message on a blackboard and holds it stiffly aloft as the cars pass on straight. Thirty seconds later, the car in question peels out of formation and slides to a stop at the pit.

The crew moves like cats. In twenty-five seconds, two tires are changed and twenty gallons of gas are force-fed into the greedy tank. Someone hands the driver a cup of Coke. The driver's face is raw with strain, his mouth a furious slit. He slugs down two swallows, barks something to the crew and braces his hands, elbows stiff, on the thick rim of the steering wheel. The pit crew pushes the car forward even before the engine blasts to life. The car rejoins The Thunder, and the crew goes limp like puppets with cut strings—an hour's energy splurged in thirty seconds.

PIT-STOP NO. 3: IN WHICH IT WOULD BE MARVELOUS NOT TO SOUND LIKE TOM WOLFE CULTURIZING JUNIOR JOHNSON:

Of all the myriad varieties of human passion, perhaps the strangest is the love of a man for a machine. Not just the love of a craftsman for handheld tools, or the obviously Freudian connection between an N.R.A. fanatic and a high-powered rifle, but passion toward a real Machine, capital "M," too big to hold, too powerful ever to be truly predictable.

So it is with the drivers who love the cars; or, more precisely, The Thunder. For, like a man mad for possession of a potent and dangerous mistress, they live for the climax—a four-hour intercourse during which they are both at the mercy of The Thunder, and its riders, lovers, tamers, hopefully its conquerers. She is the Great Bitch and she kills men without mercy when they dare to enter her vast embrace. To endure that embrace, ride it, sense its lightning-swift changes of nuance, survive it and come out winning— that is to take the Great Bitch on her own terms and beat her, make her moan for you, make her, finally, yield some of the secrets of her fury.

She is a princess with the soul of a bull dyke; she is attractive as only a mistress of goddess proportions can attract. There is a murderous grace in her power, a tidal wave's fierce majesty in the rhythms of her vitality. To win her, a man must take her as she is, brutality and beauty combined. Few men ever try, and fewer still ever gain her favors.

They don't look too glamourous, these drivers. This is not the Grand Prix circuit where the drivers tend to look like Baron von Richthofen mated to Peter Lawford. They are the boys who fill your gas tank in small southern towns, they are the guys in the garage in East Overshoe, S. C., who know what's wrong under your hood before you even come to a stop over their grease pit. Some of the best of them were born near the speedways, grew up hearing The Thunder and feeling it in their blood. They learn how to drive by driving. They start off as just one more young punk hot-rodder adding years to the life of his second-hand Ford on back-country dirt roads, cheered on by a few cronies and girl friends. More than one star driver got his basic training running moonshine down the killer back roads in the mountains and more than one who could have been a star, finished up inside a ball of anguished steel at the bottom of some hairpin curve west of Asheville.

Most of the beginners never get past that initial stage, and years later they will be sitting in the stands at Darlington wondering why and trying to ride The Thunder vicariously with the rare ones who went on. Call it obsession, lust for status and fame, call it, sometimes, the only way up and out for a country boy who knows and loves just one thing: his car and what can be done with it.

On the way up, then, they race wherever and when- ever they can—drag strips, county highways, state fairs, farm-league stock car brawls; sometimes in their own car, sometimes in a car some garage owner gave them as a grubstake investment, sometimes in a car owned jointly by several would-be drivers pooling their savings and taking turns behind the wheel. For the mediocre ones it remains just a passion, and as the years go by and they remain in the minor leagues, they drink more beer and get more cautious and start making promises that they can't ever keep; either that or they have a crack-up and their nerves go, all at once, or slowly, eroded with each compromise they have to make between fear and ambition. For the better ones, the passion becomes blended with craft, the nerves become finer, the intuition sharper and

cooler. For the best ones, the passion and the craft slowly enter a realm of physical and mental virtuosity which must be called art.

Like all top athletes, they are young. But unlike a star quarterback or a headlining infielder, they are not simply young until they become too old. While they are on top, riding The Thunder at their prime, they are young-old men in a way that transcends mere phy- sical wear-and-tear. Unlike the athlete who serves his body with his brain, the driver goes less on body-brain than on simple nerve. There inside The Thunder, at speeds which make the least miscalculation potenti- ally fatal, there is no time for mere "thinking"—there is total sensual and physical absorption with a thou- sand calculations a second. There is no time for fore- thought. Decisions are made and carried out before the brain has time to realize the process. The muscles are in a constant state of flux, battling against strains that press in from without, and an electrified tension burning rawer and rawer from within. With 200 miles of a race gone, their bodies have become comprised of 200 miles of hot-wire nerve synapses. They must be totally immersed, and yet there must always be some core of ice to hold their internal circuitry together.

Most of the good drivers leave the sport by their mid-thirties. Ulcers are a common side-effect. They must calculate and react with the speed and certainty of a computer and they must possess that rational thus-far-and-no-farther courage of a fighter pilot. The dare-devil, the hothead, the guy-with-a-grudge—either they never make it to the top, or they end up wrapped around a guard rail or flattened into a slab of concrete.

What do they get out of it, besides the satisfaction of that awful passion for their violent mistress, The Thunder? If they are good, not just good in flashes, but good over the long haul, they make good money. Fifty thousand a year is good money. If they are very good indeed, twice that is possible. Richard Petty, Golden Boy of the Plymouth fans, earned $130,000 in his best season. Then, there are commercials to be made for the gas and rubber companies, guest ap- pearances with local celebrities, interviews and pres- tige and a faint aura of legend and—if their tastes run to it—females enough to glut ten men. But most of them are family men, and even among the bachelors, promiscuity is seldom obvious. Mastering The Thunder is victory enough in the short-hair count for most men.

The rivalries are between car-and-car, usually, rather than driver-and-driver. Most of the top drivers are friendly with their comrades. Outsiders may find them reticent men, seldom really aloof, but usually a bit distant. Before the race, they stand tensely near the pits, uniformed in fireproof coveralls, going through the usual routine of autograph-signing and press interviews. After the race, or after a crack-up has forced them out, they look like men who have crawled out of a long tunnel, every mile driven shows in their eyes, in the lines of muscles that cannot believe that no more call will be made on their reserves, in the tightness of their mouths, the hair plastered flat against their skulls, the coveralls stained and limp with sweat. The winners holding their trophies and being kissed by impossibly beautiful women, the losers sucking silently on a cigarette in the shadows—the victory smiles on the former are real enough, but there is not that much difference in the eyes.

LAPS: MILE 300, DOWN TO THE CHECKERED FLAG:

The Thunder is three hours old, and there is no escaping it. It drums into the brain and, after a time, numbs portions of it. The heat is tremendous, pouring down from the sky and battering up in torrents from the asphalt and the hard dry clay. It becomes grueling just to think clearly. You wonder how the drivers can stand it. The noise, the constant dull earthdeep vibration, the heat so great that a beer inhaled with painful delight is sweated out totally in five minutes, it all combines to make everything, at this point, a little unreal. It somehow manages to be tedious, but on such a scale that there is nothing trivial involved—just a dizzying, paradoxically slow-motioned grinding against one's over-used senses.

Sometimes the brain picks out weird details. Ads painted on the sides of the speeding cars: "Golden Nugget Motel," "We Use STP," and—with a kind of hysterical inevitability—"See Rock City!"

The women in the pit area seem startlingly unreal. You expect to see them, of course, no big-time race is complete without them—wives, girl friends, camp followers, show-offs with enough connections to get a pit pass. But they appear, juxtaposed against the overwhelming masculinity of the scene, like mild hallucinations.

It's not like the Grand Prix movies, where the women in the pits all look like Francoise Hardy, move with the disdainful sexuality of pumas, and give off a redolence of six-figure Swiss bank accounts. High atop the announcer's pagoda-shaped tower, stands a *Playboy* bunny, miniskirt oscillating at mid-thigh; Infield studs jostle beneath her with binoculars, fighting for a better view. Aware of it all, she flashes them a smile slightly more inviting than a laser beam, and makes no effort whatever to conceal her riches. The impregnable disdain of her gestures is monumental, a little unnerving to see. Chicks in the pit area itself range from the drivers' wives (nervousness cooled by experience and resignation, befittingly distant from the mob, their prettiness gone a little hard at the edges), to the princesses imported for promotional color: Miss Dodge Rebellion, Miss Southern 500 and—most stunning of all—Miss Firebird. Miss Firebird is wearing one of those sadistic skirts that seems capable of hiding nothing and yet never quite goes up high enough to reveal the Big Secret. The costume looks to have been sprayed on with an air-gun. Lock a sex maniac in a room with some mahogany and a wood-

lathe and he might turn out something approximating the inhuman perfection of her legs. Pure gloss: all tits and ass and teeth and still less like Hollywood than the girl next door.

The girl next door herself, mind you, is on the *other* side of the fence, promenading around the Infield. The Infield chicks are a breed unto themselves. Their lines are hard and sharp, squeezed into tight pants and undersized blouses, their eyes a little blank except for splinters of cunning at the corners, their mouths quite often thinner than ideal, turned down a trifle into their aggressive chins, their hair teased and oversprayed to the point of being invulnerable to the worst the sun can throw at it. Their harsh consciousness of their own flesh, the frequent amplitude of their charms, the seeming honesty of their vulgarity, makes them oddly, powerfully, desirable. At their worst, they just look dumb and swinish. At their best, though, they are the primest stuff of a country boy's adolescent daydreams . . . the drive-in waitress you always wanted in high school. Miss Firebird might be better to be seen in public with, but in the backseat of Daddy's car, the Infield Girl could make her look like the rankest amateur.

Meanwhile, The Thunder is more strained, more hoarse. The last laps are being run and the crowd in the stands is on its feet because this one is going to be close, heartbreakingly close for the guy who comes in second. The tension reaches a wild peak, and then comes the release. The checkered flag sweeps down over the tortured asphalt and someone has won and many others have not and the crowd starts overflowing across the tracks to press in for a look at the winner—now hugging Miss Firebird and blinking the daze of his triumph against the popping flashbulbs of the press.

It all comes apart with astonishing quickness. The stands empty, the silence rings in your ears, the Infield folds up its tents, sweeps up its casualties, and the cars, trucks, trailers and buses all jockey for a spot in a line of traffic that stretches unbroken, north and south, for a good ten miles.

The drive out of the arena and into that traffic is anti-climactic. Perhaps, by now, anything would be. Your car crawls past a group of Wallace-for-President girls in chaste blue dresses. They all have twangy accents and tepid prettiness. If your son brought one home for dinner, you wouldn't have anything to worry about except the dullness of his taste. One of them, with large, blue, aren't-I-cute, eyes comes up to the car window and says: "Y'all wanna buy a Wallace sticker?"

"Honey, I'd rather kill my grandmother . . ."

She stares after you not with anger or reproach but with total, dull-minded incomprehension. How, she seems to be saying, can you come to Darlington on a hot southern Labor Day and *not* be a Wallace man? How indeed . . .

Suddenly it has all become terribly wearisome. The

past four hours have worn out the better circuits of your brain and you sink down into the car seat and stare glumly at the endless traffic inching its way back toward North Carolina.

Twenty minutes, and perhaps two miles, later, the car passes one of those vast stretches of Carolina field that seem to get sucked into the twilight—the sunset looks like bruised gold and the farthest pines are mysterious with that sourceless blue mist that comes, it seems, out of the deepest earth in the land and eddies slowly through the ruts and rows of the fields. Back in a copse of thick, dusty old trees, sits a slatted, crack-windowed God's-Little-Acre cabin and on its leaning front porch, a large family of Negro farmers are . . . just sitting. An old man with a stubby pipe, an old woman with bones like a dying mule, and a pack of silent black children; all . . . just sitting, their eyes gazing past the crawling lines of cars, out toward that far blue mist that comes up from the earth under the farthest rows of the pines.

You watch them until they are out of sight behind the cars. Then, you start to giggle. Because it's inevitable—it's got to happen. One of these days, if the LeRoi Jones faction can ever mesh with the Julian Bond faction, there will be a blow struck for Black Power that could topple empires. The thought will tickle you all during the long drive back: a black driver. A black driver who wins races. A black driver who wins at Darlington. Some thunder *that's* gonna be . . .

THREE TO MAKE READY

FROM A NOVEL IN PROGRESS BY MARION CANNON

When we were little girls, the twins and I, there was one thing we longed to do. After we were in bed at night we talked about it, and not one of us could find the courage to do it.

We were rarely punished. We lived with our grandparents and a maiden aunt and Mother, and the household was an adult one. How often we heard that "children should be seen and not heard"; not often, because we remembered. But if ever we did misbehave, or make too much noise, Mother would say, in a very stern voice: "Stop, children! I am two minutes ahead of a fit!" It was those two minutes that

obsessed us. We wanted desperately to push on and see the fit. We never did.

The facts about our family, as do facts for all children, I suppose, came to our knowledge very gradually. From all the bits and pieces we learned through the years, we knew that Mother had taught school when she was only seventeen and had been hired with the requirement that she put her hair up first. She had ridden bicycles when girls didn't and wore bloomers to ride in. And somehow she had seduced our father. We knew that she had run away to marry him and that they went to England. The twins, born on the honeymoon, were left in England, unknown to anyone in the little town where we lived.

No one ever talked to us about our father. We had a picture of him in our room: an old-fashioned-looking man with a dark moustache and a high, hard collar. All we knew was that he was dead: he had died when I was two, and I was almost three years younger than the twins, but they didn't remember him any more than I did.

I remembered the first time I saw the twins. It was really the first time I saw them, not the first memory of knowing them. I was sitting in the kitchen of our house, at the table with our nurse. The surrey drove into the back yard, and two little girls, exactly alike, dressed in red coats with brass buttons and wide-brimmed black hats with streamers, got out. I was told that they were my sisters. I didn't like it at all. I had been the only child, and I was spoiled. And here came two children with the fascination of being identical twins, older than I, and somehow an entity. I felt for years that there was only half of me here. They were as different in personality as possible, but there was a bond between them that no one could crack. Instinctively they leagued together against the world, most especially against me.

I suppose the twins talked to each other about where they had been before they came to live with us, but I don't remember that they ever talked to me. Not until one day when something happened and we began together to try to unravel the mystery we lived with. We had been downtown with Mother, to buy shoes or go to the dentist. We were coming home on the street car, and we overheard a woman behind us whispering to her companion: "The twin girls. . . he killed himself. . . !" The next thing we knew Mother had rung the bell for the car to stop and we got out and stood on a corner for a long time, until another street car came along and we rode home. Mother never expained what the women were saying, nor why we got off the car and waited for another. And we never asked her. But we talked a long time about it, at night, in our room. Mother was a good mother, and she did all the nice things for us that mothers can do. She read aloud to us, and played with us, and she made all our clothes from Vogue patterns. But she was a closed book to us herself.

One thing was certain, though, nothing ever got her down. And she caught another man. He brought us presents, and took us for rides in his Buick roadster, one of the first cars in our town.

We had a playroom in the basement of Grandfather's house, a dark, brick-walled room, but it was all ours. I remember one hot summer afternoon we were all down there, playing in what was called in those days "draws and bodies," a sort of camisole onto which were buttoned our drawers, with drop seats. Suddenly into the room came Mother. She did not come in as usual, with a purpose: to stop a fight, or to lay down the law, but tentatively. I remember that she was wearing what ladies called a wrapper, a long,

loose garment, and her hair was down in a braid, the way she wore it at night. She looked young.

"Children," she said, "I've come to talk to you."

"Yes, Ma'am," we answered. And there was silence.

Finally she spoke. "You know Cap, and I think you like him."

Yes, we liked him, but what difference did that make? Grown people didn't usually care how we felt, one way or the other.

"Well," said Mother in a strange new voice, soft and low, "I want to marry him."

I remember that I thought if she wants to marry him, she will. And I wondered if he wanted to marry her.

"But children, I won't marry him unless you want me to. Because it would mean a new way of living for all of us."

We looked at each other. I don't think any of us wanted to look at this new Mother, who was asking and not telling.

"He likes you," Mother went on, "and we would all live with him in another house. But you will have to tell me if you like the idea. All of us must want it."

For the first time, I believe, we were a unit, the twins and I. We didn't answer, any of us, but we moved nearer to each other. Mother looked as if she couldn't think of anything else to say. And this was upsetting. This had never happened before. She had always been so demanding, so sure, that we three had never dared say what we thought about anything. Finally Janie, the twin we all treated as if she were the eldest, spoke, "We'll think it over," she said.

And instead of an impatient "Hurry up and make up your minds," which was what we expected, Mother smiled in a soft way, then turned and left us. The universe was shattered. We had a choice to make, given to us by the ruling force of our lives. And we took it seriously. We immediately sat down on the peach boxes that served us as furniture, and went into conference. I don't remember how we discussed it, but I had a voice in it and the twins listened to me as an equal. I guess the smartest thing Mother did was to leave us. After a while we trooped upstairs, found her at her sewing machine where she turned out all our clothes, made them so fast that there were always loose threads to tickle us, on the wrong sides. She was busy. This was familiar. We gave her our consent, and she smiled absent-mindedly. "Thank you," she said, "I'm glad. Now run off, I've got to finish these petticoats."

It would be exciting to have a father. We knew that. None of us remembered anything about our own, and what we found out about him wasn't very nice. The twins had been sent for, from the Church Home in England where they had been left. He went off to meet them in New York, but didn't get there. He stopped in a town not too far from home, and went to a hotel and shot himself. I don't really blame him, though. He had gotten into a terrible mess. He just couldn't face it. And Mother must have been hell to live with.

Roy leaned against a wall in the Port Authority watching people, and after a while he went down to the Hobby Shop and looked at the electric trains. The light of the engine reflected in a tunnel. A guy stopped with a kid on his shoulders. Look at the trains, the guy said, but the kid looked at Roy. Ugly kid. Susy, look at the trains. The kid stared at Roy.

Roy walked away, took the stairs two at a time and stopped on the landing. Below, a porter was sweeping and a fat guy went by carrying boxes tied with string. Roy spit and saw the glob curve before it spattered at the guy's feet. The guy stopped; Roy smiled. Roy turned and looked at the wall: someone had written, "blow me, I'm a fuse," and "if it moves, fuck it"; someone had drawn a penis with a hair growing out of the cleft, and a breast with gushing nipples.

Roy hopped the remaining steps and fell at the top. He walked to the balcony over the lobby where some guys hung around. One had a yo-yo. Another wore a sweatshirt which said Aberdeen Proving Grounds. A black guy wore a leopard skin jacket with a green scarf. The yo-yo spooled it down at people and hit a woman.

"Hey, lady, let go!"

"I'll get a cop, that's what!"

"Aw, wet your pants!"

leaned back, holding the receiver in both hands, and yanked: the phone jingled. He banged the receiver against the dial, but it left no marks on the plastic, so he dropped it and got out. No cops, no yo-yo, so Roy went down to the Main Lobby on the escalator.

He looked in the window of the Post and Coach: a lot of soldiers were at the bar, one with his hat on sideways cutting cheese with a little knife. A dame with freckled arms sat in a booth. Roy winked and she shut her eyes.

A blonde with short hair came by carrying a big suitcase. Roy reached out.

"Hey, honey, where you heading?" The girl turned and Roy followed. "It's too big, you'll hurt yourself. I'm going where you're going."

The girl stopped a redcap, put down the bag and pointed. Roy watched her cross the lobby, then went outside. It was raining and the wet reflected the sky. A guy in a jacket with a wolf on the back shook his head.

"Oh man, crazy. Hey, gimmie a smoke?"

Roy showed the finger.

"Aw, your mother!"

Roy ran across Eighth and turned up Forty-Second. The movies made a lot of light and he looked at some pictures. A dame knelt on a bed in front of a guy in

ROY

BY JOHN LOWRY

Roy went down to a phone booth and got in. The phone was blue; the receiver hung over the dial and the cord was encased in metal. Roy took out his nail file and dug holes in the plastic covering the number. The phone rang. Loud. Roy was motionless until it stopped when he put in a dime and dialed a number. Someone answered the first ring.

"Yeah, hello?"

Roy laughed.

"Hello, hello? Come on."

"Your wife sucks."

"What's . . ."

"Eat cock!" Roy shouted, hanging up.

He sat with his hand over his mouth. Two Port Authority cops were crowding the yo-yo. The colored cop looked sharp in a blue shirt, and ribbed the yo-yo with his nightstick.

"There's a cop, no shit."

Roy pulled the receiver and the phone rang; he

a white shirt lighting a cigarette, and a cowboy in a big hat crouched behind a rock holding a gun. Then the same guy sat on a horse smiling at a dame. A nice smell came out of the lobby. Roy passed an Electric Poker place. Everybody plays, everybody wins, a guy said on a loud speaker, but the place was empty. At Wonderland, two kids watched the gypsy tell fortunes behind glass and someone rapped a bell in the shooting gallery. A hotdog place was on the corner. The counter was black and the waitresses wore green. A pimply kid stood next the window with a hotdog in his hand and two on a plate. He bit the hotdog, stuffed it into his mouth and squeezed a pimple on his neck.

Roy crossed Seventh and angled Forty-Second. A bus driver banged his horn. At Tad's, a guy in a white hat nudged steaks around on a grill. Blue flames jumped up and the steaks looked burnt. Roy went up the street. Two colored kids stopped and made faces:

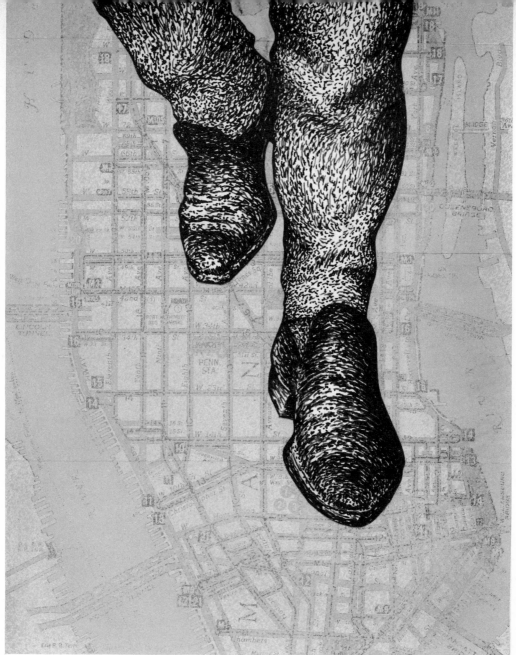

Illustrated by Robert Malone

one crossed his eyes and the other pulled out his mouth. Roy swung and kicked at the cross eyed one, but they beat it.

He saw an Automat and crossed Forty-Second again, flashing the finger at a big-mouthed cabbie. He went into the Automat. A guy in a stained jacket piled dishes on a cart and wiped off a table. Roy went to the pie window, took out thirty cents, stuck it in the slot, turned the knob and lifted out peach pie. He took a bite. A peach fell out, landing on his shoe, and Roy shook it off and squashed it. It looked black. He finished the pie and put the plate back in the window. A girl got up from a table and smoothed down her dress.

At the Hot Food counter, Roy got a tray, a plate, a knife, fork, spoon, and two napkins and skipped the lines until he got to Meats and Vegetables. A colored woman cut two and a half slices of corned beef, put it on a plate and put the plate atop the counter. The guy in front of Roy took the plate and complained: not enough beef. The woman sliced another piece.

"Corned beef," Roy said. "A lot."

The woman cut Roy two and a half pieces. He complained.

"Come back tomorrow," she said.

Roy got potatoes, peas, two rolls, coffee, and ice cream. The guy put milk in the coffee and Roy bitched.

"You say regular?"

"Come on, wake up!"

Roy paid and sat next the window. He emptied his tray and shoved it across the table. He ate, watching a black line move in the orange lights of a movie, and saw a cop in a yellow slicker ride by, his horse shifting sideways when the cop leaned over. A guy with a bowl of soup lifted Roy's tray and sat down. He wiped off his fork and spoon with his handkerchief, pulled up the sleeves of his jacket and leaned over the soup.

RED CLAY READER   103

He ate fast. Sometimes the spoon hit his teeth. He dribbled and rubbed it off with the back of his hand. He lifted out a chunk of meat, but it fell off the fork and splashed. The guy shut his eyes.

Roy ate his ice cream and watched the rain on the window. The guy finished and rubbed his teeth with his handkerchief. Roy got up. He took his plate to the water fountain and dropped it into a can full of paper cups. It made a clunk and Roy smacked his head. He took a drink. The guy at the table poured sugar into the palm of his hand. Roy beat it outside.

He stopped at a bookstore and looked at pictures of girls wrestling and guys smacking dames on the ass with rolled up newspapers. A girl in chains knelt in front of one with a whip. Lots of guys stood inside.

Roy went over to Vanderbilt Avenue. Taxis pulled into Grand Central, their horns echoing, and a limousine was at the curb with a guy in the back smiling and tanned. The Pan Am building had an arcade with benches set out of the rain and Roy sat down. The rain made a dripping; no one was around. He could see a row of desks and white vases in an airline office. A girl in blue sat near the front, cradling a phone on her shoulder and a taller girl bent over something in the back. It came up. Roy unzipped his fly and went over to the window. It felt strange, cold. He spread himself against the window, banging it against the glass. The girl looked up and Roy saw her mouth open, the phone hit the desk. Her scream sounded tiny. He zipped, holding his mouth, and ran past a guy with a dog.

"What's wrong? Stop!"

The dog barked. It needed oiling.

Roy walked when he got to Park. A guy in a red sweater said something, but Roy didn't get it. He turned east on Fifty-Fourth and saw a taxi parked at a crazy angle and two guys fighting. The tall guy had a sailor around the neck and the sailor's hat fell off when they hit the cab. A girl on the sidewalk covered her face and cried. The sailor lifted the tall guy and threw him against the cab.

"Cocksucking . . ."

A guy in a cap ran up and grabbed them.

"All right, enough. You got enough!"

The guys stopped fighting and the dame ran over to the tall guy. Roy told the sailor his hat was under the cab. He went down to the corner and looked back. The lights of the cab dimmed, then brightened.

Roy came to a hotel on Lexington. The doorman held an umbrella over an old woman and whistled at cabs.

"Morris asks for you all the time," the woman said.

The doorman watched a cab go by.

"Oh, how is he?"

Roy went through the revolving door into the hotel. A chandelier hung over a wide staircase covered with blue carpet. He spotted a Men's Room and went in. The lounge had leather chairs and dim lamps. A guy in a bush jacket sat flicking his nails.

"Want to go out of town?"

"Where?"

"Anywhere. I just want to get out of this goddamned place."

Roy walked over to a yellow machine with red knobs. In the windows were a tortoise shell comb, Sen-Sen, nail clippers and green hair oil. He pulled the plungers. A porter came in, sat down and peeled a piece of gum.

"Got a car? You want to go out of town?"

Roy went into the john. The lights made a buzz and reflected in the sinks. A urinal was running. Roy worked the handle, but the urinal screeched and ran harder. A cigarette turned in the water, leaking tobacco, and a pink disk was on the strainer. Roy went into a commode. A copy of *The Post* was stuck behind the toilet paper. The headline said a choir singer had been murdered in New Jersey, and the picture showed a pudgy dame in a surplice wearing thick glasses. On page three was a picture of a chain fence with a clump of weeds in front of it and a black arrow pointing at the weeds. The girl wore only a bra. Stabbed thirty times, in the legs, chest and stomach. Flesh had been found under her fingernails. The center fold slid to the floor and Roy dropped the rest, page by page, holding the front and back pages. Someone came in. He coughed and pissed. Roy got up, stuffed the paper into the commode and flushed. The commode made a sucking sound and stopped. The papers floated. He flushed again: the water came up and spilled onto the floor. Roy held his mouth and opened the door.

A gray-haired guy ran water over a comb, shook it, and stepped back from the sink. Roy washed his hands. He and the guy saw each other in the mirror The guy smoothed his hair and put his comb away. He leaned over the sink and lifted his nose with his thumb. Roy dried his hands, tossing the towels in the sink and ran the water until it overflowed. The guy smiled and went out. Roy lifted a towel from the sink and plastered it against the mirror.

"Who knows?"

He went through the lounge into the lobby and spun three times in the revolving door before going out onto Lexington.

It was dark. The doorman wasn't around. Cars splashed in the rain. Roy headed towards Park, stopping to look at a mural behind the counter of a luncheonette. People sat under trees at an outdoor cafe while down a long street was a slice of sky and the mast of a sailing ship. Roy turned away and saw a woman in a vinyl raincoat carrying a dog wearing a vinyl rainhat. He went down Park, through the underpass in the Grand Central Office Building. His footsteps echoed and Roy shouted. At the end was a bar with a red cocktail sign in the window and a color television in a corner. A dame at the bar was putting on galoshes and Roy saw guys in white uniforms on the television. The bartender was slapping chits on a hook next the cash register and when the guys in white started to move, he looked up.

On Vanderbilt, Roy looked across at the airline office. It was bright and empty. He went down to Forty-Second, crossed Fifth, went up the steps of the library and around the side into Bryant Park. A guy sat on the steps, making a trumpet mouthpiece sound like a bazoo. Roy watched, but the guy stopped and rubbed the mouthpiece on his knee. Roy shoved off. The trees moved and scattered light along the path. Somewhere, a guy sang opera in a loud voice. Roy sat down and looked up at the sky. The clouds looked orange.

"Shut up, creep!" a woman shouted.

Something fell through the tree behind Roy but didn't hit the ground.

He got up and went over to the steps on the Forty-First Street side. Across the street, a light in a store flashed yellow, then red. A cop went by on a scooter and his helmet looked yellow. A guy in a flying helmet without goggles came by and stuck out his hand. Roy didn't move. The guy shrugged, then lunged. Roy screamed. But the guy smiled, holding out his hand. They shook. The guy clasped Roy's hand in both of his and walked away.

Roy crossed over to the store. He banged the window, shaking the glass, and watched the light. After a while, he went up to Fifth and looked around.

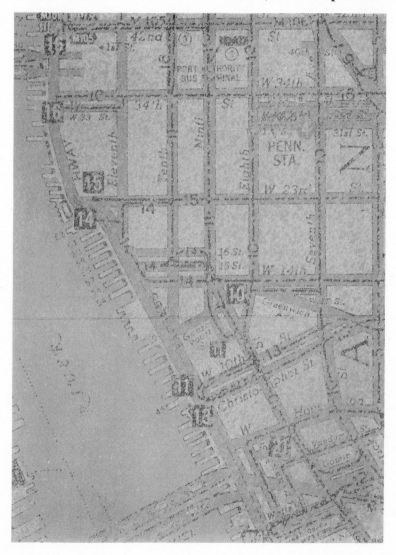

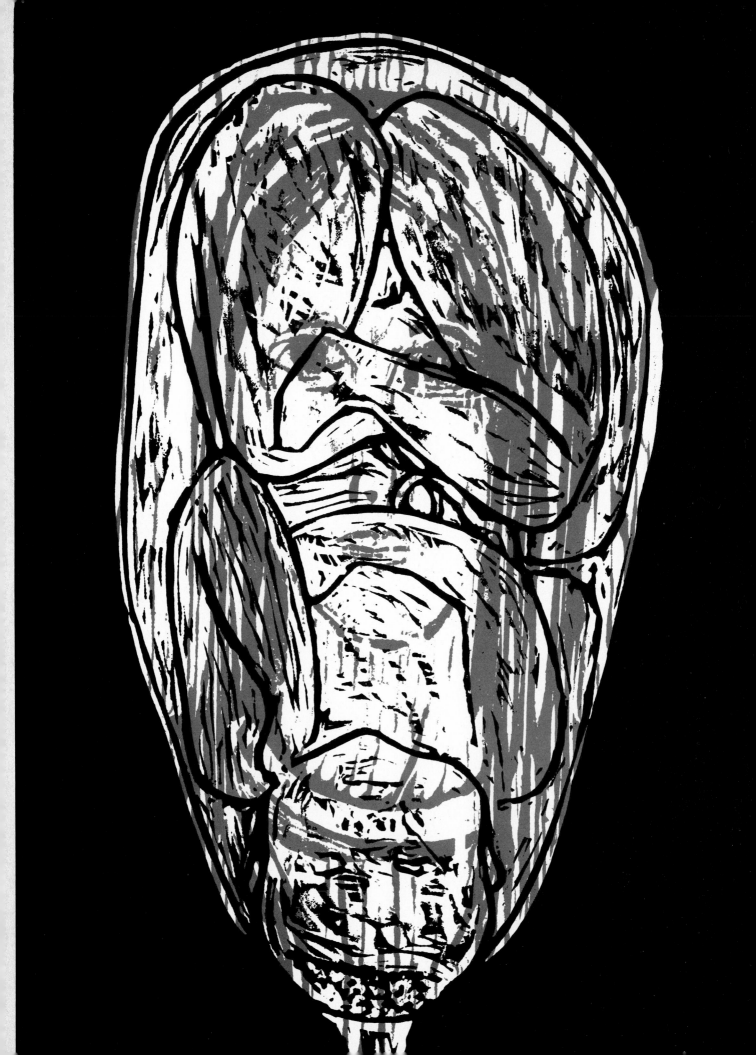

ANNIE'S LOVE CHILD

By Mark Steadman

"Best your Ma didn't live," he said, looking at the girl sitting across the kitchen table from him. "Best your Ma died before ever she should live to see this day should come."

The girl sat with her hands in her lap, motionless; her torso also motionless above the yellow oilcloth cover of the table. Her breasts were large and pendulous, outlined under the limp cloth of her dress. The dress itself was shapeless; of purple cloth with pink flowers on it. It somehow emphasized her shape without revealing it. She wore nothing underneath it, and the limp material crested at her nipples, falling straight down in two small, peaked folds. She had the tranquillity, the abidingness of a rooted thing. Of a plant that has put down roots and anchored itself in the earth. Thinking: here is the place out of which I will never be moved again. Thinking: anything which might come to touch me and to act against me would only pass over without touching the roots, and hence without any real impact nor any real threat to move me away.

"And you ain't going to say," he said. The girl didn't answer. "Just somebody come along and it happened. Just somehow it happened and you ain't going to say."

"Wouldn't do no good," the girl said. "He long gone anyway, and it wouldn't do no good."

"It would do me some good," he said. "It really would do me a whole lot of good." The girl didn't answer. "Where is he long gone to?" he said. "Where to, and where from? Annie, you answer me. You answer me and tell me who."

The girl didn't speak.

"Somebody from the carnival through here in August?" he said. "Some soldier boy from Stewart maybe? Some kind of a traveling man selling things out of a suitcase with black, shiny shoes and an automobile?"

The girl didn't speak.

"I going to find out sometime, Annie," he said, "and you might as well tell me. Sometime I going to find out anyway."

She didn't answer.

Everything about her tended downward, but downward in strength, not in weakness. Not in weariness and not in weakness. The small, indistinct festoons of the purple and pink flowers from the nipples of her

breasts; her shoulders, downward sloping but sturdy; her lank colorless hair, hanging straight down along the sides of her head, breaking into thin cascades at her shoulders and fanning slightly over the swell of her breasts. Her arms immobile at her sides, disappearing under the table.

Her eyes too were downcast. Fixed on a spot in the middle of the yellow oilcloth table cover in front of her.

The father sat cross from her. Not looking her in the eye, but meeting her gaze at the spot she had selected on the yellow oilcloth cover of the table. Bouncing his father's indignation up under her lowered lids off of the shiny yellow surface of the table. He sat with his elbows and forearms on the table before him, his hands clasped. His voice was high, with an edge on it, seeming to come from somewhere back of his mouth and above it.

"If she had of lived she would of died this day," he said, talking into the yellow shine of the oilcloth. "This day and the shame of it would have been her last had she lived to see it."

The girl's lips were relaxed. They looked like the soft, relaxed lips of a sleeping child. The man's mouth was hard, his lips thin. His lower lip projected slightly, as if he had an undershot jaw, curving back to meet the thin upper one. His mouth looked hard and dry. When he talked his lower teeth showed.

"How could you of done it, Annie?" he said. "How could you of done such a thing like that? Such a sinful thing."

She pursed her lips slightly. Not nervously, but just pursing them slightly.

"I ain't real sure yet," she said. Her voice was low, with a masculine tone in it. Low and sweet, without any hurry or nervousness to it. "Just almost two months," she said. Her lips barely moved when she spoke. "Just hardly two months. It ain't enough to tell," she said. "Not for sure."

"Tell what?" he said in his high voice. He raised his watery blue eyes to look at her face. She continued to stare at the spot in the center of the yellow table. "Tell what, when you done already told? Ain't no more telling to it. You done it and that's all. You done it and the shame ain't going to go away. Not in two months, nor in three months, nor in three years. Annie, it ain't never going to go away."

He moved his eyes down to the table again. Trying to get at her. Trying to get under the lids of her eyes to move against that rooted and vegetable passiveness.

"You think it's going to be all right if you don't have the child?" he said. "You think you can come up with your woman's blood and it just late, and that woman's blood going to wash it all away?" He worked the fingers of his hands as he talked, clasping and unclasping them on the table. "Woman's blood won't do it," he said. "Woman's blood won't wash it away like it never was. You can bleed it out for the next ten years and it won't do it."

"You sinned," he said. "You sinned, Annie, and wallowed in the filth of it, and ain't nothing going to take it away. Ain't nothing going to make it clean and take it away like it just hadn't never been."

"That's too easy," he said. "That's just too easy. And if it were so I'd go get me a swab and boil me some lye and swab the filth out of you. Swab it out and scrape it clean with a wire brush and boiling lye. I'd open you up and scrub the corruption out of you 'til you was white and dry inside. White and dry and dead, and clean of the corruption." His fingers bit white into the backs of his hands. "If it were only so. If it were only so and just so easy."

She rose from the table and began to clear away the dishes. Her hands moved surely as she picked up the dishes. The movements of her hands and arms were deliberate and unhurried as she cleared away the table things, taking them to the sink. Her eyes were still downcast. Not out of shame and not out of remorse, but out of an inwardness. As if she were looking into herself and listening to something inside, something that spoke a secret to her that she already knew but wanted to hear anyway.

The man sat at the table not looking at her.

"Leave the dishes alone," he said. "Leave the dishes alone and listen to what I got to say."

"Got to be did sometime," she said, not looking at him.

"Sometime. Some other time," he said. "Sit down, Annie. Sit down and listen to me."

"What we going to do?" he said. "What we going to do if the baby is going to come?"

She looked at him a moment. He still looking at the table, not seeing her eyes. Her eyes were calm, the lids not raised and not lowered now. Just looking at him calmly. "We going to wait and see," she said flatly. "We going to wait and see, and if the baby is going to come that's all there is. We'll just have to wait and see."

"You ain't going to have no love child, Annie," he said, his mouth tight. "For your mother's sake and her rest and peace I wouldn't let you do it."

She didn't reply.

"We going to wait a little while more," he said. "Just a little while more to be sure. And if the baby is still coming we are going to do something and stop it."

He looked at her and their eyes met.

"You ain't never going to have no love child, Annie," he said. "It ain't never going to happen."

Josey stood on one side of the kitchen table, her arms folded under her breasts. Mr. Mullins sat at the table on the other side. He looked at the spot in the center of the table. Sometimes he looked up at her. She stood erect, her head wrapped in a blue head cloth, thrown back a little, looking at him steadily.

"You too late," she said, her voice flat but distinct, not loud. "Three months is too late."

"I had to be sure," Mr. Mullins said. "Can't hardly be sure in three months."

"I could of done it with a coat hanger," said Josey. "Boiled it and scraped it right out and no trouble. But not now its too late." Small, wiry gray hairs had sprung from under the head cloth around her ears. Her apron was worn but clean. A big, yellowish brown stain splotched under the pocket, but the folds were crisp and pressed looking. She wore men's hightopped work shoes. Out of the tops of the shoes her thin shanks rose, bowing slightly up under the crisp apron.

"Three months is too long," she said. "Two is bad enough."

"We done tried the quinine," said Mr. Mullins. "And chopping wood. And I run her up and down the steps 'til I got tired watching her."

"Ain't nothing I going to be able to do," said Josey. "Ain't nothing I going to be able to do, 'cept the quinine. And that ain't going to work."

He sat looking into his hands on the table top.

"Go get me Doctor Smoaks," he said, talking to the top of the table, then looking at her. "Go get me Doctor Smoaks and bring him out here and we'll see what he got to say."

"Same thing," said Josey. "He ain't going to do nothing neither. It too late for me and too late for him too."

"I done got your say," he said. "Three months may be right. But you go get Doctor Smoaks anyway. I want to see what a white man got to say."

Josey didn't reply. She turned and walked to the kitchen door, knocking the screen open with her shoulder without unfolding her arms.

"Three months is too late," said Dr. Smoaks. He and Mr. Mullins sat at the yellow kitchen table. They were drinking coffee. Beside his cup was his black bag. Josey stood at the end of the table, her arms still folded under her breasts, moving her eyes slowly from side to side as the talk shifted between the two men.

"Maybe we could give her more quinine," said Mr. Mullins.

Dr. Smoaks lifted his cup smoothly, but daintily.

He sipped it, taking small sips, watching Mr. Mullins over the rim of the cup.

"Quinine ain't enough," he said. "Quinine ain't enough and it won't do it." He held the cup by the handle and bracing it lightly between the thumb and forefinger of the other hand. "You can give her a gallon of it a day" he said. "Pour it into her with a funnel. And chopping wood won't do it. And running her up the steps. Ain't nothing going to do it," he said. "Why don't you just face it? Annie's going to have that baby."

"No she ain't," said Mr. Mullins. "It ain't never going to happen."

Dr. Smoaks put the coffee cup back into the saucer, resting his forearm on the table. "Look at her, Dero," he said. "Just look at her and think about it. Nothing we going to do would make her turn loose of it. Can't you just look at her and see that? You couldn't even stick your hand in there and grab it and pull it out. Like as not if you tried to do it, she'd just pull down on it and hold on and bring it to term along with the child."

Dr. Smoaks pulled his watch out of his vest pocket and looked at it perfunctorily. Then he wound it and put it back into the pocket.

"Only way to get it out is to cut it out," he said. "And I wouldn't be able to do that."

Mr. Mullins looked at him. "You could do it that way?" he said.

"No," said Dr. Smoaks. "I said to cut it out was the only way it can be done. But I couldn't do it."

"She ain't but just barely sixteen," said Mr. Mullins.

"God damn it, Dero, it's against the law," said Dr. Smoaks. "I wouldn't care if she was just twelve. The law won't let you go and cut out a baby just because you feel bad about it."

He stood up and put his hand on the handle of his bag, looking down at Mr. Mullins on the other side of the yellow table. "I feel bad about it," he said. "I really do feel bad about it, but I can't cut her for you just for that."

Josey watched the two men, standing at the end of the table with her arms folded.

"What if she's going to have trouble?" said Mr. Mullins.

"She ain't," said Dr. Smoaks. "I can tell about that too. She ain't going to have no trouble at all."

"But she ain't never going to get over it," said Mr. Mullins.

"You mean *you* ain't never going to get over it," said Dr. Smoaks.

"I mean she ain't never going to get over it too," said Mr. Mullins. "Her with a baby and just barely sixteen."

"Don't nobody have to know," said Dr. Smoaks.

"How is it nobody is going to know," said Mr. Mullins. "You can't keep no secret like that."

"Maybe," said Dr. Smoaks. "Maybe so."

"How you going to keep something like that a secret?"

"I would say she had the rheumatic fever," said Dr. Smoaks. "Josey could look after her. You would keep her up in the house."

The two men looked at the woman.

"Can't no nigger keep her mouth shut," said Mr. Mullins. "I don't mean you in particular, Josey," he said, talking across the table to Dr. Smoaks, not looking at her. "Just that it ain't possible for no nigger to do it."

"Well," said Dr. Smoaks, "what choice you got? I can't do no better than that. You better think on it awhile."

"And what we going to do after?" he asked.

"I'll take care of after," said Dr. Smoaks.

"And ain't that against the law too?" asked Mr. Mullins.

"Well, yes," said Dr. Smoaks. "Well yes it is, only not as much. I would take care of after for you. I would do that."

For awhile neither one of them spoke.

"No," said Mr. Mullins at last. "No, it won't do. It's too risky. I guess you better cut her."

"I told you you I can't cut her," said Dr. Smoaks. "Get your head out of your ass and listen to me, Dero. There's a law says I can't cut her. And if I do cut her anyway, there's another law says I go to jail for it. And it probably says you go to jail for it too. And Annie."

"And the law don't care that she's not hardly sixteen?"

"Dero," said Dr. Smoaks, "the law don't give a good God damn how old she is. Nor me. Nor you. Nor Josey there."

Mr. Mullins sat thinking for a minute. "Then," he said, "I don't give a good God damn for the law."

"I want you to cut her, Smoaks," he said, his hands clasped on the table in front of him. "I want you to cut her and take the child."

"I told you I can't do it," said Dr. Smoaks. "It's against the God-damned law."

"You don't do it, I will," said Mr. Mullins quietly.

"Dr. Smoaks looked at him across the table. A quick, sharp look. "You want to kill her?" he said.

"She be better off, if it come to that," said Mr. Mullins, not looking at him.

"That's crazy talk, Dero," said Dr. Smoaks. "A strong, healthy girl like Annie. You sound like it ain't never happened before. Like Annie done outraged the whole of McClintock County this way."

"It ain't never happened before in *this* house," said Mr. Mullins. "I mean it, Smoaks. If you don't cut her, I will."

Dr. Smoaks looked at Mr. Mullins across the table. Mr. Mullins had his head down, not looking at him. His hands were clasped hard in the middle of the table.

"You reckon he means it, Josey?" he said, not looking up at the woman.

She looked at Mr. Mullins. When she spoke her voice was low and flat. "He might could do it," she said. "He feel it enough so he might could do it. I wouldn't want to say."

"You're just about that crazy," said Dr. Smoaks. "Just about crazy enough to get it started, anyway. And that would be enough. You might change your mind, and then she would bleed out right there in the bed. And you standing by wringing your hands and wishing to hell you hadn't never started in on it in the first place. And being sorry as hell after."

Mr. Mullins and Josey didn't speak.

"He might could do it," said Josey.

Dr. Smoaks didn't look at her. "You know what it looks like on the inside?" he asked. "You'd sure wish to hell you hadn't never started on it. I know that's the way it would be after it was too late. And I know you are sure as hell going to do it too. God damn it, I told you it's against the law. You want me to get my license taken away?"

"No," said Mr. Mullins. "Only I'm going to do it if you don't. Josey here will help me."

He didn't look at her, and she didn't speak.

"Yes," said Dr. Smoaks. "Oh hell yes. That'll be a fine team sure enough. Then you can both of you stand there and keep each other company while you watch her bleed to death. That'll fix it up all right."

He stood with his hand still on the handle of his bag for a minute. Then he took it off and put it in his pocket.

"Just keep him at the table 'til I get back," he said, speaking to Josey. "Ain't no rush," he said. "You got six months to go."

He went out of the screen door to the kitchen into the dark, leaving the black bag on the yellow oilcloth table.

Mr. Mullins and Josey waited in the kitchen while he walked it out. He sitting at the table, his hands clasped in front of him. She standing at the end with her arms folded.

"All right," Dr. Smoaks said, letting the screen door slam to behind him. "All right, God damn it. But if it ever gets out, I'm going to come down here some night and amputate that head off your God-damned shoulders," he said. "And the same for you, Josey," he said. "And I mean that thing."

They both looked at him, their eyes dead and waiting.

"Get some water boiling," he said to Josey. "I got to go back to my office and get the things. And make him understand he's going to watch it. He's going to watch every bit of it. He'll get himself a lesson out of this anyway. If he don't watch it—and I mean watch every bit of it—I ain't going to do nothing."

He picked up his black bag and went out the screen door, letting it slam to behind him. They heard the motor of his car roar when he started it, and the wheels spun and slung stones as he lurched it out of the yard.

Annie didn't think too well of it when Dr. Smoaks came back to see her the second time that night. And when he pulled out the needle and wanted to give her a shot, she didn't like that at all. So Mr. Mullins and Josey and Dr. Smoaks all had to kind of sit on her to hold her down while he put the needle in and gave her the shot. It took effect almost right away.

"All right," Dr. Smoaks said, dropping the syringe back into his bag. "All right, Dero, you going to have a front row seat. Right there where you can see all the blood and everything." Mr. Mullins was standing beside the bed. Between the bed and the wall. "All the blood and everything else. And when I cut it out I'm going to put it in your hand, and you're going to take it out in your hand in the back yard, and dig a hole and bury it. And the first time you close your eyes not to see, or say something, or just even make a noise, I'm going to stop right there and sew her back up and that'll be the end of it. You understand?"

Mr. Mullins didn't say anything. He stood in the small space between the bed and the wall looking down at his daughter on the bed. She looked like she was asleep, except her face was pulled down a little bit more than usual.

"You stand right there, Josey," Dr. Smoaks said. "And when I ask for something, you give it to me right away." He looked at her, "and you listen good so I ain't going to have to say it but one time."

Josey stood at the head of the bed, on Dr. Smoak's right hand side. A chair was pulled up with its back against the wall at the very head of the bed. The instruments were laid out on it on a towel.

Dr. Smoaks leaned over and raised Annie's nightgown. Josey had to help him, lifting her legs so they could work it up over her stomach. Josey turned it back down again at the top, tucking it under her chin so her face wouldn't be covered.

Mr. Mullins stood by the bed looking down at his daughter. His hands were clasped in front, hanging down, and he leaned backwards slightly, bracing his shoulders against the wall.

"I ought to shave her," said Dr. Smoaks, "but I ain't got the time. Get some of that boiled water and a rag, Josey, and wash her off good with soap."

Mr. Mullins watched.

Annie's thighs were full and slightly apart. He could see the soft rolls of flesh high up and inside them. Her stomach rose in a gentle swell. Over the fronts of her thighs and on her lower abdomen there was a down of fine, white hair. The light from the lamp beside the bed caught it from the side and turned it silver. Under Josey's scrubbing the skin turned pink, and the blonde patch between her thighs turned dark from the wet, dark golden brown, with glinting highlights from the bedside lamp.

Josey toweled her dry, and her skin had a soft, powdery texture.

"Go get some more water," said Dr. Smoaks. Josey left the room. "You swab her down with this," he said to Mr. Mullins, handing him a wad of cotton and a bottle of alcohol.

Mr. Mullins clamped the cotton to the mouth of the bottle, then upended it. He swabbed in small, rapid circles, having to lean far over the bed, because they had moved Annie near the edge on the opposite side where Dr. Smoaks could work on her better. The circles grew larger and slower. Every now and then Mr. Mullins would replenish the cotton from the bottle of alcohol. When he had swabbed her good with the circular motion, he began at the top of her abdomen, working down with overlapping swipes across from the side. He had moved one knee up onto the bed, leaning on his left arm and holding the bottle of alcohol in his left hand. When he finished he stuffed the saturated ball of cotton into the mouth of the bottle.

"Just like Mae," he said, looking down at his daughter.

"What?" said Dr. Smoaks.

Mr. Mullins looked down at his daughter's body on the bed. It was shining a little in the places where the alcohol hadn't dried yet. It had turned more pink than ever under his swabbing.

"My wife, Mae," he said. "She looked just like that. I'd forgot. Same white hair and all." He leaned back on his heel, bracing both arms on the bed. "Twelve years," he said. "I wouldn't of thought I'd forgot." He reached out his hand as if to lay it on his daughter's stomach.

Dr. Smoaks caught it quickly. "Not no more," he said. "Nothing that ain't been sterilized. Give me the bottle and stand back there against the wall."

Mr. Mullins stood between the bed and the wall, slouching his shoulders and bracing them lightly against the wall, his hands held together in front.

Josey came back into the room with a pan of water which she set down on a second chair beside the one with the instruments on it. Steam rose from the pan.

She and Dr. Smoaks washed their hands in the pan, lathering them and rinsing them, then lathering them and rinsing them again. After he dried his hands, Dr. Smoaks took a bottle of Merthiolate with a glass wand on the cap and drew a long, red line with the wand diagonally across Annie's stomach. It was a very long line, and Mr. Mullins looked at it intently. The pink in Annie's skin was fading now. She began to look pale. The red scar across her stomach was very vivid against the paleness.

"What's that?" asked Mr. Mullins.

"I cut to that line," said Dr. Smoaks. "I put the line there and cut to it so I don't forget what I'm supposed to do in the middle of it." He looked at Mr. Mullins across the bed. "I ain't no God-dammed surgeon," he said. "I ain't no God-damned high price surgeon, and it ain't every day I get to cut somebody. I figured I better draw me a picture to go by."

Mr. Mullins looked at the long, red scar. "Ain't no

growed man you got to take out of there," he said, his hands clasping tightly as he held them together. "Just a little bitty one. Hardly just big enough to see."

"You going to tell me all about it?" Dr. Smoaks asked, looking at him hard across the bed. "Why don't I just sit here and listen while you explain all about it to me?"

"It just don't hardly seem like you got to cut her that much," said Mr. Mullins.

"No telling what I might have to take out after I get her open." said Dr. Smoaks. "Might be I got to take out all kind of things after I see what she looks like inside there."

"You ain't never said nothing about that," said Mr. Mullins.

"I told you I didn't want to cut her," said Dr. Smoaks.

"But only the baby," said Mr. Mullins. "You never said nothing about taking something else."

"Can't tell," said Dr. Smoaks. "Might be I got to take out lots of things when I open her up. You never can tell about that kind of thing."

Mr. Mullins looked down at his daughter's body on the bed. The red line was very long and ugly. Sweat beaded his upper lip and he swallowed as though his throat was dry. Annie's skin had gone white again, powdery soft looking, except where it was raked by the red line of the Merthiolate.

He reached his right hand out toward her stomach, an involuntary movement. Dr. Smoaks struck it away hard, firmly and quickly.

"I told you, 'No,'" he said.

"She's my daughter," said Mr. Mullins, looking down at Annie, not at Dr. Smoaks.

"You give her to me," said Dr. Smoaks. "I didn't want her, but you give her to me."

Mr. Mullins looked up at him. "When you get through with her she's going to look like the end of a feed sack," he said.

"You wanted her fixed for the baby," said Dr. Smoaks. "I didn't say I was going to make her look pretty."

Mr. Mullins looked down at the white, dry belly of his daughter. The fine, pale hair glowed again silver in the light from the bedside lamp. "She's just like her Ma," he said. "Just like Mae used to be. I never seen it 'til now."

"Give me the scalpel," Dr. Smoaks spoke to Josey. She looked at him as he spoke, not moving. "That there," he said, pointing to the instruments on the chair.

The shaft of the bright silver instrument was poised in his hand. He held it deftly, seeming to touch it only with the tips of his fingers. Mr. Mullins clasped and unclasped his hands, licking his lips and swallowing as he watched the hand and the instrument in the hand. The dainty silver point came to rest at the upper end of the long, red slash, making a tiny dimple in the skin. Dr. Smoaks' left hand moved to rest on Annie's

hip, bracing to steady himself. He held that position, not moving for a moment. Then he made a sudden, sweeping stroke, the scalpel point just barely touching her skin. Blood started all along the red line. A string of darker beads inside the bright red of the Merthiolate.

"No," said Mr. Mullins.

He looked up and found Dr. Smoaks looking at him hard. "I ain't hardly started yet," he said. "That's just to mark the place."

"No," Mr. Mullins said. He reached down and his fingers closed around the hand that held the instrument, lifting it away.

Dr. Smoaks didn't speak.

"You get through with her she going to have a belly looks like a God-damn baseball," he said. "Stitched and puckered like a God-damn baseball. Or a God-damn feed sack."

"You going to change your mind, Dero?" said Dr. Smoaks. "You think you going to change your mind now?"

"Put them up," said Mr. Mullins. "Put them back in your bag and just go on."

"You wanted it and I'm doing it," said Dr. Smoaks.

Mr. Mullins still held his hand. He tightened his grip. "You move it and I break it," he said. "You start to move it and I break it right off."

They stood like that for a long time, reaching each

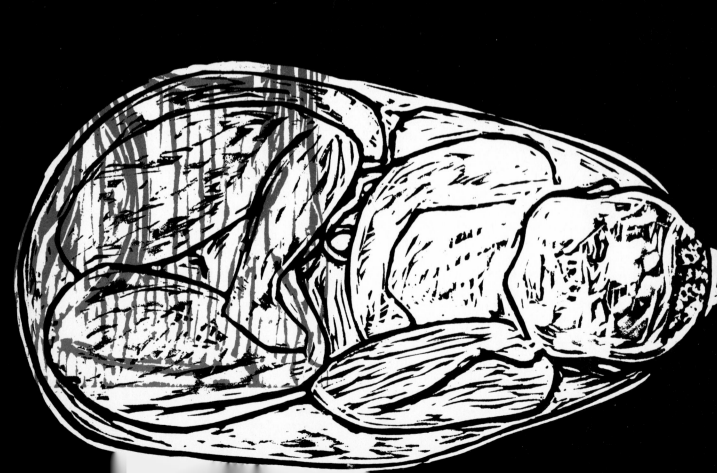

other across the bed, and across the dry, white belly of the daughter. Across the long scar stepped off with beads of dark blood inside the brighter red of the Merthiolate. Josey had folded her arms under her breasts and she stood to one side looking at them.

"It going to cost you anyway," Dr. Smoaks said at last. "You wanted it and I was set to do it. I would have done it too. So you're going to pay for it."

"Put them in your bag and go," said Mr. Mullins.

"But it's going to cost you," said Dr. Smoaks.

Mr. Mullins let go of his hand. Dr. Smoaks tossed the scalpel lightly back onto the chair. "Bring them downstairs, Josey," he said. "Bring them downstairs and get me a cup of coffee." As he walked out of the room he rolled his sleeves down. He didn't look back at Mr. Mullins.

Mr. Mullins lowered his open hand, placing it on his daughter's stomach. The red Merthiolate scar and the dark beads of blood ran out from under his fingers. Under his palm her skin was soft and dry. He removed his hand and wiped the blood on the leg of his pants.

Josey was collecting the things and putting them into the bag.

"Give me the rag," he said to her. She handed him the rag from the basin.

"Get some soap on it," he said, handing it back to her.

She soaped it and handed it back.

Mr. Mullins took the soapy rag and rubbed it along the Merhiolate scar. The beads of blood disappeared, and the bright red of the mark faded a little. But it did not disappear. Her skin turned pink again under the scrubbing.

"It go away after awhile," said Josey, looking down at him.

He looked up at her and nodded. She handed him the towel, and he gave her the rag. After he dried her, she helped him get her nightgown back down and pull up the covers. When she took the black bag and went downstairs, she left him sitting on the edge of the bed patting the cover over his daughter's stomach. He didn't look at her as she went out of the room.

When she got to the kitchen, Dr. Smoaks was sitting at the table. He had gotten his own coffee.

"Hardest case of rheumatic fever I ever diagnosed," he said, holding the cup in both hands as he sipped. "And rheumatic fever is always hard," he added.

Josey put the bag down on the end of the table and looked at him. She didn't say anything. When he finished, he rose, taking his black bag, and went to the door. Going out he stopped, holding the screen open with his hand.

"Tell him that's going to be five dollars," he said. "Five dollars whether I done it or not. Just for my time," he added.

"I would have done it too," he said, not looking at her.

Josey watched him as he went out the door.

Annie took her confinement calmly, growing even more passive as the weeks went by. Mr. Mullins insisted first that she not go out of the house, and then that she not go out of the bedroom, for fear someone would see her. Neighbors' houses were not nearby, and the loblollies screened the house from all save the few who took it in mind to make a deliberate visit, so that keeping the secret was not so difficult after all. One or two delegations of women from the neighborhood came to call, being met once by Mr. Mullins when he was home, and then by Josey when he wasn't. Holding them there on the porch and explaining that Miss Annie was poorly, and that Dr. Smoaks wouldn't allow her to have any visitors. The delegations were curious, but not persistent. They soon dropped away and didn't come back.

Josey saw to the house and fixed the meals. After she was confined to her room, Annie sat for long hours in a chair pulled back from the window—Mr. Mullins wouldn't let her come too close even there, for fear she would show herself and let the secret get away—in an attitude as of listeneng. Tracing the progress of the thing closed up inside her. Concentrated and intent on the augmentation going on inside herself, as if she were to be called on later to give an accounting for it, cell by cell.

Mr. Mullins did not try to break in on her. The night in the bedroom seemed to have cast the die for him, and he was now resigned to the fact of his daughter's condition. But her air of listening and waiting quickened him to expectation himself, and his expectation increased as her term drew to a close. Perhaps that too came out of a remembrance of what he had gone through, with Mae, sixteen years before.

"A week, maybe," said Dr. Smoaks. They sat again at the kitchen table, covered with the yellow oilcloth, Josey standing at the end of the table with her arms folded.

"She's not to have nothing," said Mr. Mullins. "No shot nor nothing to help the pain. This will be for her to learn her lesson."

Dr. Smoaks looked at him over the coffee cup. "She'll learn her lesson," he said, looking into the tilted cup. "Don't you worry about that."

"Not real hard," said Mr. Mullins. "Not real hard so as to hurt her bad. But enough for her to remember it. Just so she will learn her lesson and remember it for awhile."

"She'll remember," said Dr. Smoaks.

They wouldn't let him into the room. He sat at the kitchen table with a cup of black coffee getting cold in front of him, his hands clasped in front of him on the table, the cup of coffee between his forearms getting cold with a film of oil on top.

Every so often Josey would come down into the kitchen to do something, get some more hot water or some towels or something, and they would look at each other, but without speaking.

Finally he heard the crying. A sharp cry once, then a couple of little ones. Then nothing. He never did hear Annie making any noise.

Josey came down into the kitchen and got some more water, cold water this time, and some more towels. They looked at each other hard as she turned from the sink to go back upstairs.

"She's all right," Josey said in a flat, low voice. She didn't look at him when she spoke. From the foot of the stairs she gave him a second long look. Then she went on up to the bedroom.

In a few minutes Dr. Smoaks came down the steps. He came down them slowly, rolling down his sleeves, and walked over to the table and sat down across from Mr. Mullins.

"Coffee?" Mr. Mullins asked.

Dr. Smoaks looked up at him briefly, then back down at the table. He nodded.

Mr. Mullins got up and poured a cup of coffee at the stove. Then he put it down in front of Dr. Smoaks and went around and sat down across the table from him.

"Was it hard?" Mr. Mullins asked.

Dr. Smoaks looked up at him and then back at the table. "No," he said. "It wasn't hard. I didn't deliver it. Just caught it. It just dropped right out in my hand."

"I never did hear Annie," said Mr. Mullins.

"Annie's all right," said Dr. Smoaks. "I told you that. I told you Annie would be all right."

"I'm glad she's all right," said Mr. Mullins.

They both sipped their coffee.

"Dero," said Dr. Smoaks.

"Yes," said Mr. Mullins. "Yes, what is it?"

Dr. Smoaks didn't speak for a minute. "It's a boy, Dero," he said, sipping his coffee. He put the cup down in the saucer carefully, looking into it. They sat for a while across the table.

"God damn it, Dero," Dr. Smoaks said. He swung himself sideways in the chair, looking out the screen door of the kitchen.

"God damn it, Dero," he said again, looking down toward the floor. "It was a nigger."

Mr. Mullins looked at the side of his face across the table.

"What?" he said .

Dr. Smoaks didn't look at him. He was looking out the screen door again. "I said it's a nigger," he said. "A fine, bouncing nigger baby," he said. "Annie gave birth to a fine, bouncing nigger baby," he repeated. "A boy nigger baby."

Mr. Mullins looked at him across the table. His hands were stretched out in front of him limply, and his mouth was hanging open.

"What . . .," he said, his jaw working slowly, "What . . ."

Josey came down the stairs and into the room. She stopped at the foot of the stairs and looked at the two men.

"She wants to know can she have something to drink," she said.

"What?" said Dr. Smoaks, looking at her.

"Miss Annie want to know can she have something to drink. She say she thirsty and she want to have something to drink," she said.

"Get her a glass of water," said Dr. Smoaks. "She can have a glass of water." He was looking out the screen door again.

"Why'd you do it?" said Mr. Mullins, his voice almost too low to hear. "Couldn't you just dropped it or something?" he said. "Couldn't you just dropped it on the floor?"

"I didn't think to do it," said Dr. Smoaks. "I would have done it if I had thought to do it. But I was too surprised to think about it I reckon," he said. "It was just that I had it in my hands, and then it was breathing on its own. And it started to holler, so I couldn't think what I had to do until it was too late. It was already hollering and it was too late."

"What you mean it was too late?" said Mr. Mullins.

Dr. Smoaks looked at him. "I mean it was too late," he said. He didn't explain.

"It ain't too late for me," said Mr. Mullins. He scraped back his chair and rose from the table.

Dr. Smoaks looked up at him across the table. "She ain't asleep," he said. "You said she wasn't to have nothing, so she ain't asleep. You going to play hell getting it away from her."

Mr. Mullins stood in front of his chair.

"Anyway," said Dr. Smoaks, looking away again, "it ain't that easy. Even if you do get it away from her," he said. "It ain't that easy."

He rose, scraping back his chair. "Well," he said, "anyway I'm through with it—finally."

"What?" said Mr. Mullins. "You said you was going to take care of it." He looked at Dr. Smoaks.

"I can't get rid of no nigger baby," he said.

"You said you was going to fix it up and take care of it," Mr. Mullins said.

"Not no nigger baby," said Dr. Smoaks. "I can't get rid of no nigger baby. See Josey," he said. "Maybe she get rid of it for you."

"I'll get rid of it," Mr. Mullins said, not looking at Josey.

"All right if you can," said Dr. Smoaks. "You take care of it if you can. It ain't that easy. Not even a nigger baby is that easy."

He rose, taking his black bag in his hand and going to the door. He stood with the door held open a little, not looking back at Mr. Mullins.

"You owe me a dollar," he said, standing in the door. "My fee for delivering a nigger baby is one dollar," he said. "So you owe me one dollar."

He went out of the house, letting the screen door slam behind him.

He bowed the hickory stick between his hands,

standing at the foot of the bed, watching Annie nurse the baby. She watched the baby, not looking at him.

"You going to give it up," he said. Bowing the stick out in front of him. "I don't mean you going to give it up next week," he said, his voice breaking into the darkness of the room. "Not next week, nor some other time," he said. "I mean you going to give it up now."

Annie watched the brown head against her breast. It made her breast look even whiter, with the pale blue veins just under the skin.

Mr. Mullins whipped the stick across the end of the bed. It sounded like a rifle going off in the still room. Annie flinched, but she didn't look at him.

"I mean now," he said, louder.

He struck the bed again. Not hitting anything, just the bed. He whipped the stick down again and again, the tempo increasing and the noise of the slaps getting louder. Saying, "Now . . . Now . . . Now!" And the stick hitting in between. Annie flinched every time the stick hit the bed. But she didn't look up at her father. The stick broke, and Mr. Mullins tried to whip the bed with the stump. It was too short and he threw it against the wall.

"Now," he said.

"Let her finish with the baby," Josey spoke from the doorway of the bedroom. "She be through in a while," she said. "That be time enough."

He stood at the foot of the bed watching. His eyes held tight on the brown head against the blue-white of Annie's breast.

Josey spoke again from the doorway. "Why don't you wait 'til she be sleep? She got to go to sleep sometime," she said.

Mr. Mullins paid no attention to her. "He's through," he said, after awhile. He came around to the side of the bed, keeping his eyes on the brown head as he moved. "He's through, ain't he?" he said, looking down as he stood by the side of the bed.

Annie didn't look at him. The baby didn't move. The nipple had come half out of his mouth and his eyes were closed.

"You got to take him?" Annie's voice was low and there was just a little quaver in it. She didn't look up at him.

"Yes," he said. "I got to take him now," he said.

He reached down and lifted him up. Annie's arms were limp outside the covers. She didn't move to cover her breast, and after he moved the baby away Mr. Mullins stood looking down at the whiteness of his daughter's breast, with the nipple still moist and pink from the sucking, the veins pale blue just under the skin. He held the baby away, one hand under its head and the other under its hips, looking down at her in the bed.

"He's too little," she said.

"Cover yourself," he said.

She drew the sheet over her breast, pulling it up to her chin. "He's too little," she said again.

"You got to give him up," he said, holding the baby away and looking down at her. "You got to give him up now, because you ain't going to want to do it no more tomorrow, not the day after, nor any other time. Now is the best time," he said.

"Same as killing him," she said.

"It's be on me," he said. "All of it'll be on me."

He continued to look down at her.

"You knowed you wasn't going to keep it anyway," he said. "Not if it had been like I thought, you wasn't going to keep it. And you sure as hell knowed you wasn't going to get to keep it like it is."

He started toward the door, still holding the baby away from him. Holding it in his hands so it wouldn't lay against him and touch him.

"Pa," she said from the bed. He turned and she was looking at him now. "Pa," she said again, still looking at him, "his name is John Henry." After she said it she looked away from him.

"That's what he needs," said Mr. Mullins, looking back at her. "That sure is just what he needs now. Put that name on him and fix him up for sure."

"Well," he said then, "put it on him if you want to. You can put any name you want to on him. It don't make no difference. He ain't never going to know anyhow. So just go ahead and put it on him."

"Pa," she said, looking at him again. "Josey," she said looking away. "Make him put the bunting on him, Josey. So he don't catch cold."

"Yes, child," said Josey from the doorway.

He walked out of the room and down the stairs, still holding the baby away in his hands to keep it from touching him.

It was getting lighter all the time, and still he hadn't made up his mind. He would have to make it up soon though, since he had to get done with it and back to the house before it was good light.

The bank dropped off steeply in front of him. The black water undercut the bank, and little eddies floated by in an arc, reaching in toward the roots hanging down into the water. Mr. Mullins was sitting and looking down into the water, his back propped against a tree. Beside him the baby lay on the sack. The sack was spread out on the ground, but there was a bulge in the bottom of it where he had put the rocks. The baby fidgeted but it didn't cry. Every now and then it would flinch its arm or its leg and screw its face up, but so far it hadn't cried. Mr. Mullins kept thinking that if it would only cry he could do it. And he got mad since the baby wouldn't cry. He sat there leaning against the tree and getting madder all the time. Looking at the black water swirling past under the bank.

Mr. Mullins would look at the water and then he would look at the baby beside him. Streaks of mist hung under the trees along the opposite bank. The water looked cold, but he knew it was warm. He had reached down and put his hand in it to see.

"Shit," he said, finally standing up. "Shit on it anyway."

"Out of the county," he said, handing the baby to Josey in the kitchen. It was full light now. He had taken a long time getting back because he had to stay away from the cleared land for fear someone would see him. "That's all I give a good God damn about," he said. "Just make sure you get him out of the county."

"Yes, suh," said Josey, flatly, taking the baby from him and cradling it in her arms. "I see to it," she said.

He went to the cupboard and took out a Prince Albert tobacco can. "Here," he said, handing her the money. "Two dollars is all I can spare. You do it for the two dollars, you hear?"

Josey took the money without speaking, but she nodded her head.

"I ever see him again," he said, "and I going back to the river. I going to take him back to the river and do it," he said. "Won't happen twice."

Josey nodded and turned to leave, the baby cradled in her arms.

"And, Josey," he said. She turned to him. "Better not nobody ever find out," he said. "Better not nobody ever find out, or I take you with me I go back to the river."

She looked at him a minute, then turned and went out the kitchen door.

"You better get back in that bed," he said. Annie stood at the foot of the stairs. He sat at the kitchen table, his forearms stretched out on the yellow oil-cloth top, his hands clasped together. He looked at her then back at the table. "You get back in the bed," he said. "You get back there and stay 'til you get your strength back. Then we see what we going to do."

"He was too little," she said, looking at him from the foot of the stairs. "You wasn't even going to use the bunting 'til I said it," she said. "If you just could of waited a little bit."

He didn't look at her. "Won't you please get back in the bed, Annie?" he said. "We going to have to talk about it later on. But won't you please get back in the bed right now?"

She looked at him from the foot of the stairs. Her bare feet were planted on the floor firmly, and with her hand she reached out, just barely touching the newel to steady her. Her lank hair was hanging down over her breasts and she looked pale. Under her hair the milk was making two long, weeping stains down the front of her nightgown.

"His name is John Henry, Pa," she said, her voice low and level from the bottom of the stairs. "I give him his name," she said, "and his name is John Henry."

He didn't look at her. "Won't you please get back in the God-dammed bed?" he said He put his head down on the edge of the table between his elbows. His voice was muffled and low. "Won't you please, Annie, get back in the God-dammed bed?"

She looked at him a minute, then turned and walked slowly up the stairs. Leaving him resting his head on the shiny, yellow table in the kitchen.

John Lowry

Edward Minus

Photo by Andy Warhole

Photos by Jim May

Coleman Barks

Elizabeth Oakes

Gerard Malanga

Harry Martin

William Harmon

Doris Betts

Colette Inez

Gary Gildner

Marion Cannon

Robert W. Hill

Jonathan Morse

John Satterfield

Lloyd Davis

Lyn Lifshin

Greg Kuzma

FICTION

Doris Betts' most recent book is *The Astronomer & Other Stories*. She is the author of two novels and is currently teaching creative writing at the University of North Carolina at Chapel Hill.

Marion Cannon had a story in RED CLAY READER I. She is now writing a novel.

John Lowry teaches at Pratt Institute, Brooklyn, New York. He has been published in *Georgia Review*.

James Mechem was born in Wichita, Kansas and is still there, working in publications for Beech Aircraft.

The Greyhound Minstrel is Edward Minus' first published fiction. He teaches at Spartanburg Junior College in South Carolina.

John Satterfield is a jazz musician and composer. His fiction has appeared in *Perpective, Epoch,* and *Southern Humanities Review*. He is now Vice President for Academic Affairs at Elmira College in New York.

Mark Steadman was born in Statesboro, Georgia and is now teaching at the American University in Cairo, Egypt. *Annie's Love Child* is his first published fiction.

Laurel Trivelpiece was born in Nebraska and now lives in California. Her poetry and fiction have appeared in various little magazines and she is now at work on a novel.

Sylvia Wilkinson has taught at William and Mary and the University of North Carolina. Author of *Moss on the North Side,* she is at work on a new novel.

NON-FICTION

William Trotter spent three years doing the Young-Writer-In-New York routine until the literary agency representing him got bought-out by a parking lot corporation. Appropriately embittered, he has returned to Charlotte and the drudgery of free-lancing.

Roger Wicker was born in 1944 and grew up in Asheville, North Carolina where he worked as a copy-editor on the *Citizen*. He is now Director of the Center for Curriculum Design at Kendall College in Evanston, Illinois.

Jonathan Williams is a poet and a publisher. He was at Black Mountain College from 1951 to 1956 and is currently Director of *The Jargon Society* at Penland School. A selection of his poems, *An Ear in Bartram's Tree,* was recently published by the University of North Carolina Press.

Sylvia Wilkinson is the author of two novels. Her stories have been published by *Mademoiselle* and in *Southern Writing In The Sixties*. Miss Wilkinson teaches at the University of North Carolina and is currently Writer-in-residence at Hollins.

POETRY

Coleman Barks' work has been in the *Ann Arbor Review* and *Tennessee Poetry Journal*. He is now teaching at the University of Georgia, and a selection of his poems will appear in the forthcoming Doubleday anthology: *Some Poets of the 1970's*.

Rebecca Brown was born in Southern Pines, North Carolina. She is now in school in New York City and her poetry will appear in *Sanskaras*.

Skip Burns is a graduate of Rollins College. He now teaches at Gaston Day School in Gastonia, North Carolina.

Lloyd Davis is the Editor of *West Virginia University Magazine*. His poems have appeared in the *Georgia Review*.

David Galler is the author of two volumes of poetry, *Walls and Distances* and *Leopards in the Temple*. He has recently published in *The Yale Review, The New Yorker,* and the *Quarterly Review of Literature*. He lives in New York City.

Gary Gildner lives in Des Moines, Iowa and teaches at Drake University. He has had poems in *The Nation, Antioch Review* and *December*. His first collection from the University of Pittsburgh Press is titled *First Practice*.

Emilie Glen is a New York actress. Her poems and stories have been widely published and anthologized by *New Directions* and *Best American Short Stories*.

William Harmon is an officer in the United States Navy and taught at Annapolis. He was born in 1938 in Concord, North Carolina and now lives in Deer Park, Ohio.

Robert W. Hill is on leave from Clemson University to work on his Doctorate at the University of Illinois.

Colette Inez was born in Brussels, Belgium. She is now teaching in the New York City Anti-Poverty Program. Her poems have appeared in *Shenandoah, Prairie Schooner,* and *Southern Poetry Review*.

Greg Kuzma lives in Slippery Rock, Pennsylvania.

Lyn Lifshin grew up in Middlebury, Vermont. She will have a volume of poetry from Open Skull Press called *Why is the House Dissolving?* and a record from Folkways, *After it All Happens Again*.

Amon Liner was born in 1940 in Charlotte, North Carolina and attended Kenyon College. His poetry has appeared in *Folio* and *Foxfire*.

Gerard Malanga is an actor and an Executive Producer for Andy Warhol Films, Inc. He is the author of five books and his poems are scheduled for *The Paris Review, Evergreen Review, Partisan Review* and *The Yale Literary Magazine*.

Harry Martin is now doing graduate work in history at St. Louis University. He lives and teaches in Central America.

Peter Meinke has published a critical study of Howard Nemerov and has recent poems in the *Michigan Quarterly* and *Epos*. He is now teaching at the University of Sussex in England, on leave from Florida Presbyterian College.

Jonathan Morse will have a collection of poems in the anthology *The Smith Poets*. He graduated from Penn State in 1965, in bacteriology.

William Trotter

Peter Meinke

Rebecca Brown

Ken Higdon

Phil Morgan

Mary Mintich

Robert Malone

Ethel D. Guest

Donald Miller

Joe Thompson

Elizabeth Oakes is 26 years old and lives in Bowling Green, Kentucky. She graduated from the University of Iowa and has her first published poetry in this issue of RED CLAY READER.

Terry Stokes work will appear in *New Generation of Poets*, Black Sun Press. He is 24 and teaches at Western Michigan University in Kalamazoo.

Roger Weingarten is co-editor of *Confluence Magazine*. He is 23, teaching and studying at the University of Iowa, Writers Workshop.

Chris Lamson-White is an actress who was educated at the University of North Carolina and now lives in Washington, D. C.

GRAPHICS

George Bireline teaches in the School of Architecture at North Carolina University. His paintings have been exhibited in several one man shows at the Emmerick Gallery in New York.

Walter Charnley is a film maker who won the Seattle Festival prize. He is currently working on a documentary in New York's Lower East Side.

Maud Gatewood was born in Yanceyville, North Carolina and attended Ohio State University and the University of North Carolina at Greensboro. Her work has been widely exhibited and she is now teaching on the Charlotte campus of the University.

Mike Goins has had paintings in the North Carolina State Museum and the Mint Museum. He graduated from East Carolina University and is now teaching at Rose High School in Greenville, North Carolina.

Ethel D. Guest studied at A. & T. State and Boston University. She is teaching in Charlotte.

Ken Higdon was born in Tennessee. He is a self taught illustrator and film maker whose films have been exhibited throughout the United States and Europe and are in the collection of the Museum of Modern Art.

Robert Malone teaches art at West Virginia University in Morgantown. He exhibits widely and has won many national awards.

Wes McClure was born in Pendleton, South Carolina in 1946. He graduated from North Carolina State in architecture and is now in the Navy.

Donald Miller graduated from East Carolina University in 1966. He is now teaching art at East Mecklenburg High School.

Mary Mintich was born in Detroit. She has exhibited regionally and nationally and is currently teaching at Sacred Heart College in Belmont, North Carolina.

Phil Morgan has been a photographer for newspapers and television. Born in Wilmington, North Carolina he is now working at the *Charlotte Observer*.

Joe Thompson attended the Philadelphia Museum College of Art. He recently had a one man show at the McDonald Gallery in Charlotte.